601567

D1217803

THE NEW FORCE

The New Force

The Story of Atoms and People

by RALPH E. LAPP

Foreword by Stewart Alsop

Harper & Brothers Publishers

New York

TO

PROFESSOR ARTHUR J. DEMPSTER

Contents

Foreword

by Stewart Alsop

It is ten years now since the first chain reaction took place, and the scientists of the Manhattan District first began to pry open the nuclear Pandora's Box. In those ten years, the real nature and meaning of atomic energy have been consistently obscured by sensationalism or wrapped in mystery. Yet there is no subject which anyone who wishes to form a reasonably informed judgment on the state of this nation and the world needs more to understand. And there is no subject so little understood.

The hush-hush atmosphere which has quite unnecessarily surrounded atomic energy has caused a sort of Victorian reaction to the whole subject—it is a subject which is "better not discussed." Many people, moreover, after the first burst of sensationalism subsided, seem to have concluded that atomic energy is a bit of a bore, and at any rate no concern of theirs. Both attitudes are dead wrong.

Even to a total scientific ignoramus like the present writer, atomic energy is a subject of extraordinary fascination, once a few not very formidable scientific hurdles have been overleapt, as I believe readers of this book will discover for themselves. What is more important, atomic energy has, for better or for worse, changed the essential nature of the world in which we live. It is easy to forget—and it is often forgotten, in the State Department and even in the Pentagon—that the real world balance of power is now determined by atomic energy more than by any other single factor. In this sense, a man who does not know the essential facts of atomic energy is a man who does not know the essential facts of the world situation.

In short it is time, and past time, for a book which treats this subject sensibly, understandably, and accurately. This is such a book. And Dr. Lapp is the man to write it.

I know that he is the man to write it, because I have collaborated with him on four long and rather difficult magazine articles, all dealing with one aspect or another of atomic energy. Always in the end—although frequently at the price of a few headaches —Dr. Lapp has succeeded in causing the basic facts essential to an understanding of atomic energy to penetrate my ill-prepared brain. In the 25,000 or so words published under our joint by-line, no one, as far as I know, has yet found an error of scientific fact. In *The New Force*, it seems to me, Dr. Lapp has been able to present the facts of atomic energy clearly, readably, and yet with complete scientific accuracy. Anyone with the intellectual curiosity—and, in a sense, the courage—to want to understand what our atomic age is all about can, I think, for the first time find in this book what he is looking for.

THE NEW FORCE

1

ABOUT PEOPLE AND ATOMIC ENERGY

T<small>HIS</small> is an age of television, jet aircraft, automatic gadgets, and miracle drugs. It is also the age of atomic energy. Pandora's wonderful box has been pried open by science to enhance the twentieth century with many material benefits. We can see most of these things or at least know that they contribute to our better way of life here in the United States.

Most of these things do good work for us—in the case of television they even amuse us (sometimes) and inform us (less often). So almost everyone agrees that these are good things. But what about atomic energy? Is it a good thing or a bad thing? I suppose if you are one of the over hundred thousand living near an atomic plant and getting a weekly paycheck because of our atomic program you will say it is a good thing. But the chances are that even if you work at one of these plants in Oak Ridge, Tennessee, Hanford, Washington, Paducah, Kentucky, or in the billion-dollar plants near Aiken, South Carolina, and Portsmouth, Ohio, you would have no better basis except a paycheck for sizing up atomic energy.

Atomic energy has become a thing apart from the American conscience. Too many Americans have been conditioned to think of this new force purely as an instrument of destruction. Atomic energy in the minds of many is symbolized by "the bomb." This is like thinking of petroleum as something which can cause fires and explosions, forgetting its myriad uses in providing us with power and with petroleum derivatives such as lubricants and drugs. The atom, too, can provide us with power and with important derivatives, such as radioactive materials. However, no wheels in American industry are being turned today by this new force, no street lights are burning on atom-generated electricity, and only a very few people have benefited from atomic by-products. Therefore, atomic energy is a big unknown to the average American.

I would like to take the reader with me and act as his guide, showing him both sides of the atom—its peaceful and its military potential. Preferably, I would like to show him only the peacetime promise of atomic energy but in these troubled times this would be unrealistic. It is highly important that the military aspects be illustrated.

Before we set out on this exploration I feel that the reader probably has some questions to ask of me so I shall put some words in his (or her) mouth and then try to provide some answers.

The reader may well be pardoned for asking: "Isn't this subject of atomic energy too technical for a layman to understand?" There are two points I would like to emphasize here. One is that you do *not* have to be a scientist to understand atomic energy as it affects (or may affect) the lives of individual citizens. You will find no mathematical calculations in this book. Furthermore, there is a minimum of foreign language that I shall use and each new term in this discussion will be defined. The other point is that I have had some experience as a lecturer and magazine writer and I am confident that atomic energy *can* capture the imagination of an intelligent audience.

Another question the reader may be asking himself: "How can we explore the atomic field? Isn't it all too secret?" I would be very glad if that question were asked, for I would not like to misrepresent. There are places and things I shall not write about, but these constitute only a very small fraction, I would say less than 2 per cent, of the territory to be covered. The reader may have some curiosity about knowing how an A-bomb is put together, but I am sure that he will agree that such things properly belong in the secret category. In the years that I have been writing and speaking on atomic energy I have never given away an atomic secret even though I worked for the government for over six years and had access to much top secret data. I have reviewed every sentence in this book to make sure that there is nothing which compromises the national security. By cross checking against material previously agreed upon by officials in the Atomic Energy Commission I have weeded out things which might be of aid and comfort to an enemy. Yet, and this may be rather surprising, this weeding operation does not detract from the finished product.

Later on I shall have a great deal to say about this matter of atomic secrecy for I believe that many of the security restrictions imposed upon the atomic energy field hurt it more than they can possibly help. Many officials in Washington have a weird concept of what secrecy is. The result is that if you were to ask one of them for an escorted tour of the atomic territory it would be a mighty quick trip. In fact, I do not think that you would even get your ticket punched. Were I still a government employee I should probably have to give the reader the same treatment.

The "atomic age" is over ten years old now, but many Americans may wonder just what atomic power is, when we will have it, whether it will mean free electricity, and whether it is dangerous in any way. Surely many want to know about atomic engines and how they will propel ships at sea or, someday, aircraft. And, on the grim side, people naturally wonder (and worry) about the modern atomic explosives, about the H-bomb, and about the atom destroying the world.

In fact, it was just such a series of questions which caused this book to be written. In knocking about the country giving lectures at universities, clubs, and public affairs I always allowed time afterward for questions from the audience. I usually felt a sense of frustration that in the short time at hand I could only answer such a few of the many questions that people asked and that I could not go into questions which I wished they had asked. So I thought of this book as an after-hours way of presenting the information in an orderly and more detailed fashion.

About the same time that I was dreaming about the book, the editors of Harper's were also thinking about such a publication. They spotted one of my magazine articles and we got together. Together we examined a list of current books in the field. Of course we already knew about, or discovered, a good many excellent titles—some by top-flight scientists and writers—but none which seemed to attempt an up-to-date and comprehensive report for a general audience.

So I agreed to do the book. Fortunately, the publishers felt as I did that it should be a down-to-earth factual account and not a version highly inflated with the sensationalism which has attended atomic energy since its birth. Then, as I settled down to actually work on the manuscript I realized that it was strategically a wonderful time to tell the real story of atomic energy. There was the broad spectrum of ten years of atomic energy to cover and before the book was finished the whole expanded atomic program in this nation had taken shape so that it could be described in full. Furthermore, the H-bomb had risen above the technical horizon along with other developments so that one could write with some confidence that his words would not be obsolete before they were off the press.

Mine was a very modest role in the atomic energy picture and I hope that you will not think me immodest in injecting here and there some personal anecdotes. It was my good fortune to be in on many big events in atomic energy among outstanding men and I hope that the personal touch will communicate something of the wonderful nature of this new field. Science is nothing without the admixture of the rich personalities of the men who so wholly dedicate themselves to it. In working during the war to develop the atomic bomb and let the new force out into the world these men drove themselves tirelessly to complete the job that had to be done. To let the Nazis get the bomb first might be to lose the war; to delay our getting it by even so much as a day might mean additional sacrifice of American lives. After the bomb had been used and the war was over some physicists felt a sense of guilt at having helped to unleash the new atomic force which could so terrorize civilization. But they should have no guilt complex for the bomb would have been made anyway. Perhaps not by us and perhaps not so soon, but it would have been made.

In this connection I recall a very prophetic speech by the noted British scientist Dr. F. W. Aston. The speech made in 1936 concluded with the remarkable prediction:

There are those about us who say that such research should be stopped by law, alleging that man's destructive powers are already large enough. So, no doubt, the more elderly and ape-like of our prehistoric ancestors objected to the innovation attending the use of the newly discovered agency, fire. Personally, I think that there is no doubt that subatomic energy is available all around us and that one day man will release and control its almost infinite power. We cannot prevent him from doing so and can only hope that he will not use it exclusively in blowing up his next-door neighbor.

What Dr. Aston clearly implies is that science, itself, is neither good nor evil. The end products of science—television, aircraft, and atomic energy—are thrust upon civilization with a neutral gender. It is what man does with them that determines the good or evil aspect for many of the products of modern science are mixed blessings. Aircraft can be used for rapid civilian transportation or they can be used to rain down bombs on another nation. Atomic energy can be used as a weapon or as a new source of power. Even the hydrogen bomb now appears to have a brighter side, for some competent scientists feel that the H-bomb project will yield peacetime benefits. So, perhaps, even in the case of this terrible weapon Abe Lincoln's philosophy relative to whisky applies. He felt that the harm arose not "from the use of a bad thing, but from the abuse of a very good thing."

Man must learn to live with this new force. As the late Senator Brien McMahon expressed it:

The hard fact is that the American people simply cannot ignore the split atom. It will shape our destinies irrespective of our wishes. There is no half way house. We control the atom or it controls us. The matter is too fundamental to be left solely in the hands of officials designated to direct our atomic program.

2

THE NEW FORCE

Tracking down the origin of the new force—atomic energy —is not too difficult if we mean by it the splitting of the atom. If we think in more general terms the origin is more diffuse and takes us back fifty years to the days when Albert Einstein worked in a Swiss Patent Office and first propounded his theory of relativity. About this theory we need to know no more than that part of it leads to the conclusion that mass and energy are interchangeable. The mathematical relation $E=mc^2$ has become so commonplace that the author need only explain that E stands for energy, m for mass, and c^2 is the square of the velocity of light.

While mass and energy are interconvertible one should not jump to the conclusion that this is something which can be done in the kitchen. Energy can be released from matter only under quite special circumstances. Splitting of the atom or "fission" as it is called is a special event which permits a small fraction of the mass of a heavy uranium atom to be changed into energy. Nowadays we accept uranium fission as an ordinary event. People near the atomic test range at Las Vegas seem to be little disturbed when an A-bomb is detonated there. But back in the 1930's fission was far from being an ordinary event. In fact, it was so extraordinary that then even the most brilliant minds in atomic science could not bring themselves to conclude that fission was possible.

Let us look back some two decades into the preatomic era when our atomic scientists and those in foreign lands were just beginning to sense that something big was in store for them in atomic research. Uranium was just an element found in glistening pitchlike pitchblende ore in the Belgian Congo and in a few other spots. It was chiefly used as a source of radium and to a limited extent as a pigment for ceramics.

Enrico Fermi, the soft-spoken Italian-born physicist, who now is a professor of physics at the University of Chicago, was then at the University of Rome. Together with his colleagues he was intensely interested in finding out what happened when various substances were bombarded with tiny nuclear particles called neutrons. These particles had been discovered in 1932 by Sir James Chadwick in England. When a pea-sized lump of radium was encased in a beryllium sphere the size of a golf ball it was found that rays from the radium knocked neutrons out of the beryllium. The combination of radium and beryllium formed a convenient portable source of neutrons. It was not something one could leave unattended for the rays could do serious damage to anyone who happened to linger nearby for too long a time. Normally, the neutron source was placed in a lead vault when it was not in use. This shielded passersby from injury.

(8)

Being of an inquisitive nature, Fermi exposed many substances to the rays from this neutron source. Nothing escaped his imagination. He wanted to find out if the neutrons would not stick to atoms of the materials he was bombarding and create entirely new atoms. In many cases this happened and new atoms were created and identified by the fact that they were radioactive. They gave off radiation which could be measured with instruments such as Geiger counters. One day, the Italian experimenters bombarded uranium with neutrons. This was a dramatic experiment for uranium is the heaviest, most complex element that occurs in nature. They reasoned that when they bombarded the uranium with neutrons it might capture the particles and convert itself to a still heavier and entirely new element. This would be element 93 lying beyond uranium (element 92) in the periodic system of elements.

These bombardments with uranium were made in 1934. Fermi and his associates discovered that the bombarded uranium was made radioactive. In fact, there were four distinct radioactivities so they assumed that these were due to four different species of new elements. They thought that for the first time on earth elements heavier than uranium had been created.

The race to investigate these new transuranium elements was now on. In France and in Germany scientists repeated Fermi's experiments over and over. The results were essentially confirmed. Even more new radioactivities turned up and these were quickly assigned to more new elements until the list stretched up to element 97. Three of the German scientists actively studying these assumed-new elements were Otto Hahn, Lise Meitner, and F. Strassmann. Part of their interest lay in chemically separating out the new elements and in identifying their properties. These investigators had worked for years with every element under the sun and they applied all their skill and ingenuity to isolating the new elements. During their long drawn-out experiments they had little doubt that what they were seeking were pure elements heavier than uranium. They were so close to the forest that they didn't see the trees!

Then the unexpected happened. Hahn and Strassmann made an astonishing discovery. When they carefully analyzed the elements which they thought belonged to elements 93, 94, 95, and 96, they found that one of them proved to be barium. Now barium is a middle-weight element having number 56. No two experimenters were ever so sorely puzzled. How could a mere neutron striking an atom of element 92 produce a medium-weight barium atom? They repeated their experiments, carefully checking the results. They reached the same conclusion. At the time (the fall of 1938) they were working at the Kaiser-Wilhelm Institute for Chemistry in Berlin and they modestly described their results in *Die Naturwissenschaften,* a leading German scientific magazine. But despite the fact that they positively identified barium resulting from neutron bombardment of uranium the two distinguished scientists were "in contradiction to all previous experience in nuclear physics," reluctant to say that they had split the uranium atom. But split it they had!

However, the explanation of what Hahn and Strassmann had done came from Lise Meitner and her nephew O. R. Frisch who was working at the University in Copenhagen. Frau Meitner had fled from the Nazi tyranny in Berlin and had been welcomed at Stockholm. Together with her nephew, also a refugee from Nazidom, she pieced together the nuclear jigsaw puzzle and saw clearly that the results of Hahn and Strassmann could be explained by a daring assumption. In a letter to *Nature,* the weekly British science journal, the two scientists stated: "At first sight this result (that of Hahn and Strassmann) seems very hard to understand." They went on to explain that "An entirely different and essentially classical picture of the new disintegration process suggests itself." This new scheme which they proposed was that the uranium nucleus (the dense core of the U-atom) was composed of many particles which together behaved as a liquid drop. When this droplet was agitated it was set into violent motion. To continue with the account given by Meitner and Frisch, "If the movement is made sufficiently violent by adding energy such a drop may divide itself into two smaller drops. It seems therefore possible that the uranium nucleus has only a small stability of form, and may, after neutron capture, divide itself into two nuclei of roughly equal size." To this process they gave the name, "fission."

Why should this fission of a uranium atom release energy? Why was not fission observed in other elements which had been bombarded with neutrons? How did this atomic energy manifest itself?

Answering the first question is relatively easy although it may take a while for the reader to grasp the basic significance of what is meant. When a single atom of uranium splits into two lighter atoms roughly equal in weight we know that a relatively large amount of energy is released. Since energy and mass are interconvertible this must mean that the split halves of the uranium atom must add up to less weight than the original unsplit atom. Physicists have special instruments with which to weigh even things as tiny as atoms. When they weighed the split halves of the uranium atom they found that the total weight was slightly less than the unfissioned U-atom. It is this slight difference in weight which is converted into energy when a uranium atom is fissioned.

Now for the next question. Why did only uranium undergo fission when bombarded with neutrons? Actually thorium also fissions but only uranium fissions when struck with neutrons of low energy. Other elements like phosphorus or sodium captured neutrons and were made radioactive but they did not split apart as did uranium. They did not release energy. It turns out that of all the 92 known elements only uranium, element 92, will fission when struck by slowly moving neutrons. The technical explanation of why this is so would require that the reader acquire some knowledge of how the various atoms are put together. It is sufficient to state that the internal structure of some uranium atoms is such that the addition to them of a single neutron adds enough energy to set them into violent motion and rend them asunder.

This brings us to the last of this trio of questions. And in a very real sense it can be phrased: "Just what is atomic energy?" We answer this by considering that we could peer down into a uranium atom as it is struck by a neutron and see what happens. In a twinkling of an eye the neutron is swallowed up by the massive uranium nucleus. Instantly the hard core of the struck uranium atom is set into motion. It vibrates like the oscillations of a tiny drop of water released from the tip of a medicine dropper. In no time at all these drastic oscillations deform the nucleus so much that it looks like an elongated dumbbell. At this point the tenuous connection between the two halves of the stretched uranium atom vanishes and fission takes place. Now the two halves of the split atom fly in opposite directions with tremendous speed. Both fragments have a speed of about 10,000 miles per second or about 30,000 times the velocity of a rifle bullet. Unlike rifle bullets these tiny nuclear fragments do not travel very far in air. They lose speed very quickly and are completely stopped in roughly one inch of air. Inside solid uranium the split-off fragments travel even shorter distances of about one-thousandth of an inch. But in this short race that the fragments run they impart tremendous energy to other nearby atoms and this energy appears in the form of heat. Thus atomic energy released in fission appears as heat energy. There is absolutely nothing mysterious about it.

To return to the chronological detail of the fission story we take up the sequel to the Meitner-Frisch explanation of the Hahn-Strassmann experiment. Frisch immediately set to work to demonstrate that the split atom fragments from uranium should be readily detectable so that the fission explanation could be verified. He lined a small metal chamber with uranium and bombarded the chamber with neutrons. Fragments produced by the uranium fission shot through the gas of his chamber and were detected by means of an electronic amplifier. In a few short days the fission theory was verified experimentally.

The first month of 1939 saw Frederic Joliot independently making careful experiments on uranium fission. His results, published in the French journal *Comptes Rendus* on January 30th, paralleled those of other scientific workers. Nuclear physics laboratories all over the world soon buzzed with activity as physicists quickly threw together apparatus to investigate nuclear fission.

Word of the German discovery was quick to reach the United States. Prior to publication of the results the data on fission were communicated to Niels Bohr, the famous Danish theoretical physicist. He arrived in the United States in mid-January and immediately divulged the information to scientists at Princeton and Columbia Universities. The news spread like wildfire. Enrico Fermi who had left Italy to accept a position at Columbia University lost no time in setting to work in the physics laboratory on the campus. Within two weeks American scientists and scientific refugees from Europe gathered in Washington, D. C., for a scheduled conference. Fission was the big news at this conference. It infected scientists with impatience to return to their institutions and to begin new research on uranium. Enthusiasm was not confined to purely scientific circles for word got around to the newspapers that something big was in the wind. Thus in the very first month when the discovery was announced the public got wind of the new development. The January 29th edition of the *New York Times* carried a brief mention of the Washington scientific conference and introduced the word "fission" to newspaper readers. Two days later an edition carried the lead "VAST ENERGY FREED BY URANIUM ATOM." The story gave an account of the German experiments and stated that they had been repeated at Columbia University on January 25th with the aid of the newly installed cyclotron.

Digging back into the dusty newspaper files of 1939 one is struck with the frequent mention of uranium fission. The discovery was listed as the outstanding development in science for that year and it was heralded as the equal of the discovery of radioactivity. One newspaper story had a prophetic ring for it gave the tip-off on the A-bomb. Published on page 35 of the April 30th edition of the *New York Times* the essence of the story may be summed up in a brief quotation: "Dr. Niels Bohr of Copenhagen declared that bombardment of a small amount of pure isotope 235 of uranium with slow neutrons would start a 'chain reaction' or atomic explosion sufficiently great to blow up a laboratory and the surrounding country for many miles." Many physicists disputed Dr. Bohr's contention but it must be remembered that the Danish scientist was widely regarded as one of the three greatest scientists of the twentieth century. His words deserved serious attention. Later, during the war, Dr. Bohr was to escape from beleaguered Denmark and return to the United States to help make his prediction come true.

Two phrases in the *New York Times* quotation may be unfamiliar to the reader. They are "isotope 235 of uranium" and "chain reaction." These two phrases constitute the key to the release of atomic energy so we shall consider each one carefully.

We must backtrack some four years in our chronicle to a scene which took place on the University of Chicago campus one day in 1935. There in a darkened room of a physics laboratory the late Professor Arthur J. Dempster was quietly doing a bit of atomic research which we may call isotope-hunting. A slightly built, almost excessively shy, individual, Dr. Dempster had been studying how the various elements are composed by analyzing them in an intricate atom-sorting machine which he had devised. The instrument was a mass spectrograph and with it one could look at all the atoms of any element and measure how much they weighed. With such devices scientists had discovered that some elements like gold have atoms which are all equal in weight. Others have different weight atoms—we call these *isotopes*. Tin, for example, has the most isotopes of any element, having a total of ten. A tiny sample of tin slipped into the business end of Dempster's machine, ignited to super white heat, and analyzed in the complex instrument gave ten visible lines on a photographic plate, each line corresponding to an isotope of tin.

This day in 1935 Professor Dempster was experimenting with uranium. Until then it was thought that it was all composed of one single isotope which we symbolize as U-238. In other words uranium atoms were all the same weight—this weight being indicated by the number 238 which is an index of its total weight. Carefully the Canadian-born physicist adjusted the uranium inside an evacuated glass tube and then he stepped aside and threw a switch turning on the high voltage. Then 15,000 volts of electricity hurled uranium atoms from the glass tube into the inner parts of the apparatus. Standing close to the glass tube with his nose only inches away, Dr. Dempster watched the bluish sputtering glow inside the tube as the atoms raced across the vacuum space. The room was in total darkness so as not to fog the photographic plate. Eerie shadows flickered over the walls until finally the scientist flipped a switch cutting off the voltage. Then he groped in the total darkness to retrieve the photographic plate with whatever secret it held in store, slipping it into a cardboard light-tight box. A few minutes later, having developed the plate, he snapped on a small bulb in the adjoining dark room and scanned the still milky emulsion. Despite his years of similar research, Dr. Dempster always had an almost childlike impatience to see what he had "caught" in his machine so that he couldn't wait until the plate was fully cleared by the chemical solution. Holding the plate up against the light he saw the dense line made by the U-238 isotope. Then, he blinked and looked closer. There was a faint line close to the U-238 just discernible on the plate. Making a mental note that perhaps it was an impurity he placed the glass fragment back in the chemical-fixing solution and went back to his office. Although he had later to make careful measurements to identify the line and prove that it belonged to the element-uranium, this marked the discovery of U-235, a rare isotope of uranium.

Coming as it did four years before the discovery of fission, the announcement of the finding of U-235 as a rare isotope of uranium caused no great excitement. It was another isotope and

Dempster had chalked up many isotopes to his list of discoveries. Almost five years later a group working at Columbia University under Professor John Dunning, now Dean of Engineering there, discovered that the fission found by Hahn and Strassmann in bombarding uranium with neutrons was produced by U-235 and not by the 140-fold more abundant U-238. Dr. Alfred Nier from the University of Minnesota had succeeded in separating a tiny sample of U-235 from uranium and the group at Columbia exposed this to neutrons. Their results showed that U-235 and not U-238 was the culprit responsible for fission. This was in line with a theoretical prediction made by Niels Bohr and Dr. John A. Wheeler, a young theoretician at Princeton.

Of all the isotopes of the 92 elements that exist in nature, and there are some 280 of them, only one fissions when struck by slow neutrons. This means that this one isotope, U-235, is the keystone of atomic energy. Yet uranium ore contains only 1 part of U-235 for 140 parts of U-238. We shall see in the next chapter how difficult a feat it was to separate the U-235 from the more abundant U-238. Unless U-235 could be so separated and obtained in a pure form no atomic bomb would be possible with the material. Natural uranium as it came from the mine could not sustain an atomic explosion.

How was an atomic explosion to be realized? To make a single uranium atom explode was one thing. To make a sizable chunk of uranium explode meant that a good fraction of the atoms inside had to be split at the same time or almost at the same time. This was the puzzler which confronted the scientists as soon as fission had been discovered. Enrico Fermi was one of the first, if not the first, to see that the neutron was the solution. Neutrons were the "open Sesame" to fission. If the fission process, itself, released neutrons then one might be able to make these neutrons cause more fission and so on in a repeated chain of fissions. Thus was born the concept of a chain reaction.

Early experiments showed that when a U-235 atom fissioned some neutrons were shot out of the split atom. This was an epochal discovery rivaling that of fission itself although its importance is not generally stressed. Without these neutrons a chain reaction would be impossible. Nuclear fission like any other nuclear reaction would be a single-shot affair, releasing energy it is true, but requiring some continuous outside influence (neutrons or cyclotrons) to make the reaction go. Neutrons released in fission made all the difference in the world for they linked one fission to another in a chain of events so that one might start a self-perpetuating reaction. Since the neutrons travel with lightning speed inside even solid matter one could theoretically start a chain reaction inside a chunk of pure U-235 and create an atomic explosion.

The big question then arose: "How many neutrons arose out of each fission?" If there were less than one per fission then a chain reaction would not be self-perpetuating. Analogous to the growth of man's progeny, if there were less than a certain number of offspring per generation the line would die out. If there were, say, two neutrons per generation (that is in each fission cycle) then the neutrons would multiply and fission would flourish. In this circumstance we might say that the chain reaction had a high reproduction or multiplication factor. When physicists first set to work to ascertain how many neutrons were emitted in the explosion of a single U-235 atom they got vague results for the measurements were not then very good. It seemed that the number was somewhere between one and three. An average of all the prewar measurements gave 2.3 neutrons per fission. Later measurements made during the war were more exact and showed

(18)

that 2.5 neutrons were released but this bit of information was held secret until 1950. Then it was decided that the Russians had made an A-bomb of their own so they could not have but measured this value accurately. Obviously, one cannot hope to keep such a thing secret for anyone who seeks to find out has only to ask the questions of nature in the form of experiments and the answer will be forthcoming. In this case the answer was very hopeful for the ultimate perfection of a chain reaction.

Scientists all over the world eagerly turned to fission research during 1939. Testimony to this fact is the publication in scientific journals of about one hundred scientific papers on fission and fission phenomena. The field of atomic research was yet to know the blight of secrecy. Scientists were just beginning to realize that they were tinkering with the mainspring of nature's most potent energy source. A few sensed that this new force which they had uncovered would be of military significance and they, of their own volition, invoked strict secrecy in their publications so that Nazi Germany would not be apprised of the U.S. developments. Curiously, these men were primarily the foreign-born scientists who had fled from Europe to escape persecution under totalitarian regimes. Stellar scientists such as Enrico Fermi from Italy, Albert Einstein from Germany, Hans Bethe from Germany (Alsace-Lorraine), Leo Szilard, Edward Teller, and Eugene Wigner all hailing from Budapest were all to play a leading role in the A-bomb project. These men were among the first to urge the U.S. government to use the atom's potential as a military weapon.

One March day a meeting was arranged between Enrico Fermi and representatives of the Navy Department. Calmly and in a matter of fact way, this leading scientist modestly briefed a group of military men on the implications of fission. Perhaps

Fermi was too vague, perhaps the Navy brass regarded him as a visionary, whatever the cause the Navy issued a polite thank you and said it would like to be kept on the mailing list. So the first attempt of scientists to enlist aid from the military was not capped with success.

The pay-off came when a really high level approach was tried. Stimulated by the two Hungarian-born physicists Wigner and Szilard, Professor Einstein sent a personal letter dated August 2, 1939, to President Roosevelt. In it he outlined the need for government interest in the uranium work. The President responded to Einstein's appeal and the first governmental committee on atomic energy was established. This committee met for the first time on October 21, 1939, and discussed the possibilities of using the chain reaction for producing an explosion and for producing controllable power. It made certain recommendations for accelerating uranium research and as a result the Armed Forces dug up $6,000 for support of the work.

This may seem like a paltry sum to appropriate for such a momentous project but back in the fall of 1939 no one was sure that an A-bomb could be made. No one was sure that a chain reaction could be made to work. There were too many things which physicists needed to know before they would hazard more than a guess about the eventual success of the project. Fission had only just been discovered and much exploratory work had to be done to pave the way for large-scale work which was to follow. Then, too, science and the military in the United States represented a new partnership. Each member of the new team was cautious, more than a little afraid of the other, so the uranium work did not.go forward at full speed.

Would we have had the A-bomb much sooner if at this time the Army had launched an all-out effort? It is a question of academic interest but it also strikes close to the heart of the problem of how a scientific development is best nurtured. Perhaps a few months could have been shaved off the timetable for getting the A-bomb if greater priority had been assigned to the project in the early days. On the other hand one must remember that in the earliest days of fission our scientists were feeling their way across an unknown terrain. Had they been forced to speed across this tricky territory rather than been allowed to take their time and look for minute hidden signposts to point the way they might well have lost rather than gained time. In science the bulldozer approach is not always the best one. Our initial progress in atomic energy during the prewar period did not depend upon having millions of dollars and thousands of construction men. Rather it was keyed to the mental activity of a very few top scientists who were probing their way along uncharted trails. The rate of progress depended upon the inspiration and judgment of our intellectual giants.

Steadily the scientists grappled with the multitude of problems which confronted them. But with one significant difference. They divorced themselves from the time-honored free interchange of information with other scientists and in 1940 they voluntarily imposed secrecy upon their work. Reports had filtered through from Germany that Hitler had authorized an atomic energy project. Our own scientists were fearful that unless we kept our work secret from the rest of the world the Nazis might be aided in their own project. Throughout the development of our bomb project this nightmare of a Nazi A-bomb was to haunt our activities and to goad our men into greater efforts.

We were not alone in our attack upon the atom. Apart from what the Germans might be doing, scientists in England were busily at work on their own atomic research. Sir James Chadwick, the brilliant discoverer of the neutron, spearheaded the British work. In typical British fashion he and a few colleagues patiently examined every conceivable aspect of the release of energy through fission. Then in the winter of 1940 they began systematic studies of U-235 to see how well the material would work as a bomb ingredient. They recognized that there were a score of factors which might make it impossible to attain a chain reaction with U-235. Not until the summer of 1941 were they sure of their facts. Sir Chadwick wrote: "We were satisfied that the project of making an atomic bomb was practicable and likely to lead to decisive results in the war." This was the gist of the report which was officially submitted to the British government, recommending immediate large-scale operations to make an A-bomb.

During the early British work there was some co-operation with the United States but in Chadwick's own words, "It was not very effective." This was very much to the detriment of the United States for the British had made significant strides ahead in their scientific approach to the uranium work. In failing to co-operate with the British valuable time was lost. Just how much it is futile even to guess but had we shared our knowledge with the best brains in England we could have undoubtedly accelerated the pace of the work. Secrecy, about which we shall have more to say in a later chapter, actually impeded our progress. We forgot then, and we seem to have forgotten today, that the best form of security is the rapid prosecution of a new development.

There will be those who, peculiarly endowed with 20-20 hindsight, will argue that if we had never collaborated with the British on the A-bomb we would never have had to deal with the traitor Dr. Klaus Fuchs. This twisted genius even in 1941 was transmitting secret atomic data to the Russians. But we did not know this until some eight years later. No one should attempt to minimize the heinous nature and serious magnitude of the Fuchs' disclosures but it is gross exaggeration to maintain that "Fuchs gave the A-bomb to the Soviets." This point will be amplified in the chapter on secrecy. We must not forget that at the time our enemy was Germany not Russia. Our main concern was to lick the Nazis, and then later the Japs. On the basis of intelligence data available in this country we erroneously deduced that we were in a neck-and-neck race with the Nazis to get the A-bomb. Therefore, we had to do everything we could in order to bring the uranium project to a successful conclusion in the shortest possible time. Pooling our resources with the British significantly shortened the time required for the pay-off of our A-bomb project.

One way to appreciate the British contribution to the A-bomb project is to look at the European parentage of the A-bomb. Too often Americans are bedazzled by the hugeness of the plants at Oak Ridge and Hanford to appreciate that these are but brute force accomplishments of an engineering type. Behind them lay the all-important scientific principles which mainly evolved from Europe. The basic platform upon which the American bomb was built was provided by the genius of Lord Rutherford in England, Professor Einstein in Germany, the Joliot-Curies in France, Fermi in Italy, Hahn and Strassmann in Germany, Bohr in Denmark. The list grows very long and includes almost every country in Europe and Russia as well.

Had we in America tried to push our atomic project to its conclusion without the direct aid from many European scientists we would never have tested an A-bomb in 1945. Using only American-born simon-pure scientists we would have hamstrung our atomic project. This statement is not meant to deprecate the quality of American science or to conclude that Americans alone could not have made an A-bomb. But it is almost certain that without the genius of "foreigners" like Fermi, Bethe, Wigner, and Teller—to name but a few—it would have taken much longer to get the bomb. Time after time in the history of the bomb project it was one of these foreign-born scientists who came up with the bright idea or the new angle which allowed us to vault an impasse. When one stands on the banks of the broad Columbia River and surveys the sprawling agglomeration of mammoth atomic plants at the Hanford site one's first impression may be, "What a tremendous industrial accomplishment this is!" Less obvious is the hard fact that of even greater importance was the brain work which such men as Fermi, Wigner, and Szilard—all Europeans—put in to make these plants possible.

Just as these Europeans made invaluable contributions to our progress so, too, did a select group of scientists imported from Britain serve to speed up our work on the bomb. At the Los Alamos laboratory, where the atomic weapon was fabricated, a handful of British experts were instrumental in devising techniques for detonating an A-bomb. Secrecy still has not been relaxed sufficiently to permit even a partial account of how such British scientists as shock-haired Dr. W. G. Penney aided in this work. Additional contributions of the British were investigations of processes which were used at Oak Ridge to separate U-235 from uranium.

Partly because of the British optimism about atomic energy, partly because of similar American optimism, and probably in large measure because of the shadow which the war was casting across the Atlantic the decision to give a go-ahead on the atomic project came up late in 1941. Scientific and technical aspects of the project had been thoroughly reviewed by groups of scientists when Dr. Vannevar Bush went to the White House to put the matter before President Roosevelt. At the time Dr. Bush was Director of the Office of Scientific Research and Development, an agency created by the President to mobilize the nation's scientific reserves in preparation for the threat of a world war. He was able to tell the President that atomic energy had evolved from the think stage. Scientists who had formerly held that an A-bomb might be possible now were convinced that a nuclear chain reaction could be achieved. Some top scientists were impatient with authorities for not pressing for larger-scale operations sooner. Perhaps they would have been less precipitous had they foreseen the many obstacles which were to crop up during the next three and a half years. Nonetheless there was a strong feeling of confidence about the prospects for atomic energy and Dr. Bush must have managed to convey much of this to the President for he responded magnificently. He gave his personal approval to an all-out program and made available funds for program expansion from his emergency kitty.

The day before Pearl Harbor, Dr. James B. Conant, the president of Harvard and Bush's strong right hand, was able to announce to a committee of the Office of Scientific Research and Development that an all-out effort had been authorized. At the same time he announced that work was being placed under the direction of the O.S.R.D. Thus on December 6, 1941, our atomic project crossed the Rubicon. As if to dramatically reiterate the urgency for the all-out effort the next day news of Pearl Harbor spurred scientists to rush headlong into the task of making the A-bomb—the most challenging single task ever delegated to a group of scientists.

Almost overnight scientists became "big operators." Previously glimpsed only on the college green, physicists were to be seen, if you could recognize them, scurrying in and out of Washington. Atomic science had become big business and scientists were suddenly cast in a new role. They played their parts modestly and well, planning multimillion-dollar projects and unheard of construction tasks as though they were quite used to such Olympian tasks. Gone were the days when as department heads they worried about a glassblower's salary, the purchase of a drill press, or scraped the bottom of the barrel for money to buy a transformer.

This prewar period was remarkable in that the total span of two years had seen the split atom emerge as a laboratory curiosity and become a potentially decisive instrument of war. Never before had time been so abridged. But never before had the need been so great. New weapons were required to check the onrush of Hitler's blitzkrieg. The need was underlined by the war in the Pacific where we would have to strike at an enemy across vast stretches of the Pacific. But to most scientists the big question was "Could we get the bomb before the Nazis?" However, it must be admitted that there were some doubting Thomases who wondered whether we could make the bomb at all. During the next three hectic years there were to be many roadblocks interposed between the scientists and their final objective. There were to be times when it seemed that nature conspired to tantalize man with the rare fruit of atomic energy but, as with the mythical Tantalus, always kept it just out of reach. In the days following Pearl Harbor, scientists gathered all their strength for a concerted attack upon the atom.

3

FROM MANHATTAN TO NAGASAKI

THREE and a half years after Niels Bohr brought the news of fission to America the War Department established its now famous Manhattan Project to make the atomic bomb. Known as the Manhattan Engineer District, this project gained momentum when Major General (then Brigadier General) Leslie R. Groves took command.

The job ahead was utterly unlike any which had ever confronted the military. The big job was to produce bomb material. Before the task was completed the project was to spend almost $2 billion and to build huge production plants which by the war's end wrested from nature less bomb material than you could put in a gallon bucket. But such was the nature of the problem that you had to go whole hog to get this seemingly insignificant amount of material. What really staggered the military mind was the blithe confidence with which atomic scientists talked about building huge production plants that would stretch over acres of ground. All this, mind you, had to be done when the nation was engaged in an all-out war and materials and man power were hard to get. This, by itself, would have been perplexing enough but the truly incredible aspect of this huge construction program was that the plants to be built involved processes which either were still to be tested or were tried only on a test tube basis.

Despite the many uncertainties surrounding the work to be accomplished the over-all program was clearly defined. There were two principal objectives. One was to perfect processes and build plants for producing the bomb material. The other was to learn how to make an A-bomb. In the matter of a bomb material there were two choices. The most obvious was U-235— the scarce and difficult-to-separate isotope of uranium. Less obvious and a challenge to the imagination was the alternate bomb material called plutonium.

Our story of the Manhattan Project will be trisected. First, we shall consider the Oak Ridge saga which we may label the U-235 story. Second, we shall recount the highlights of the Plutonium Project. Finally, we shall look briefly at the story behind the development of the A-bomb, itself.

At first glance it would seem that the separation of U-235 from uranium ore might not be too difficult. One had only to strip off U-235 from U-238 and the job was done. However, this was a colossal "only." To begin with one had to get the uranium ore. Within the boundaries of continental U.S.A. there were limited deposits of rather low-grade ore. The Mother Lode of uranium ore was located in the depths of Africa, a thousand miles in from the coast in the Belgian Congo. Here were found pitchblende veins rich in the lustrous uranium ore. These fields had never been worked to their capacity for prior to the Manhattan Project there had never been much of a demand for the ore. Suddenly, with the emergence of uranium as a critical defense material the Belgian Congo became of enormous importance to the United States. Diplomatic arrangements were concluded between Belgium and the United States to permit exploitation of the Mother Lode. Shipments of the now precious ore were speeded to the United States but figures on the tonnage of the mineral have never been released. All data about what the Atomic Energy Commission calls its primary raw or feed material are kept secret even today.

Our friendly next-door neighbor Canada turned out to be a good friend, indeed, for in its Great Bear Lake region there were good workable deposits of pitchblende. While they were not as rich as those in the Belgian Congo, none the less they were a welcome addition to our uranium stockpile. They were something we could fall back on and exploit to the hilt should the Atlantic supply line fail to maintain the flow of ore from Africa.

Having the uranium ore the big step to take was to contrive some method to separate the wheat from the chaff. In the case of uranium the "chaff" was the 140-fold more abundant U-238 isotope. Back in the spring of 1939 when atomic scientists first looked at this problem many of them declared that the task was virtually impossible. They argued that while there were techniques for winning the U-235 from uranium they were such low-return processes that they would be prohibitively expensive. Physicists had to drastically revise their estimates of what "expensive" really meant for none of them had ever dipped very deeply in the nation's coffers.

One of the very biggest difficulties which confronted the scientists in the U-235 separation problem was that there were at least four, possibly more, ways to solve the problem. However, until you plowed through a vast research program and built fairly large-scale pilot plants you could not be sure which process would really work. Imagine the chagrin of Army officials when they undertook the Manhattan Project assignment in the summer of 1942 thinking it was a straightforward construction-production job, only to discover that the fundamental plant processes had yet to be tested in practical operation.

The four separation processes were: gaseous diffusion, thermal diffusion, electromagnetic separation, and the centrifuge method. All appeared theoretically possible even as they also promised to be time consuming and fearfully expensive. It is beyond the scope of this report to explain or even describe each of these four separation processes except to mention that all of them had one thing in common. All depended for their operation upon the fact that U-238 weighed 3 units more than U-235. It was upon this tiny weight difference that the ultimate success of the separation processes would depend. Since both U-235 and U-238 belonged to the same element there was no chemical technique that could be used to dissolve out one isotope at the expense of the other. Skipping over the history of the work on the four separation processes and the heart-breaking effort which went in to proving that certain techniques would not work we can focus attention upon the one process which paid off best. This was the gaseous diffusion process.

The principle of the gaseous diffusion process can be explained quite simply. Imagine that you have a long tube and in the middle of it you put a material which has tiny porous openings. On one side of the porous barrier you pump in the uranium in the form of a gas. Now as the U-235 and U-238 molecules come in contact with the tiny openings in the barrier the U-235 molecules diffuse or migrate through the openings at a rate which is slighter faster than that for the heavier U-238 molecules. This is because the U-235 molecules being lighter move faster and have a slightly better chance of getting through one of the tiny openings. Thus if you have a barrier with just the right size holes in it you can achieve a very slight separation of the two isotopes, for the molecules passing through to one side of the tube will contain slightly more U-235 molecules than those on the other side. We say that the gas which passes through the barrier is slightly enriched in U-235 content. It is as though the tiny openings in the barrier had a low-grade intelligence and acted with preference for the lean U-235 atoms and an aversion to the opulent U-238 atoms. However, the preference for the U-235 atoms is very slight and in one pass through the barrier the gas is enriched in U-235 by only 1 part in 1,000. By circulating the gas through thousands of separate barriers gas can be obtained which is practically pure U-235.

All this may sound simple and one might jump to the conclusion that A-bombs could be made a dime a dozen. However, from an engineering viewpoint the gaseous diffusion method presented many headaches. First of all the only gaseous form of uranium is an extremely corrosive and dangerously toxic gas called UF_6, uranium tetrafluoride. This gas is produced from the solid uranium ore by chemically treating the uranium oxide to produce the green-colored fluoride. No ordinary pipes would last long filled with this gas. Specially fabricated leakproof tubes had to be made to contain the noxious gas. Then, leakproof, corrosionproof pumps had to be made to circulate the gas within the thousands of miles of pipes required for the diffusion plant.

But the biggest obstacle of all was the design and production of the porous barriers. The porous plug was the key to the diffusion method and unless it could be manufactured to a high degree of perfection the diffusion method would not work. The barriers constitute one of the still-unrevealed "secrets" of the A-bomb. They are specially prepared materials uniformly permeated by fragile submicroscopic holes less than one-ten-millionth of an inch in diameter. Large-scale operation required a multitude of these barriers. The number was calculated to be such that the total barrier surface would cover over an acre of area. To pull the gas through the tiny holes in the barriers thousands of high power pumps were required.

All in all the diffusion plant represented an exceedingly tough engineering assignment. One of the largest steam power plants ever designed had to be built to provide power for the pumping system. The many miles of stainless steel pipes had to be joined together so that the system was leakproof. So rigid was the requirement for being airtight that special instruments had to be invented to test each section of pipe for airtightness. Ordinary methods were too crude so a special instrument known as a helium leak tester was rushed through development and put into production.

Even before the technical problems were solved and before pilot plant operation had been completed a seventy-square-mile section of the Tennessee Valley was singled out for the construction of the diffusion plant. The site is well known today as Oak Ridge although during the war it was nicknamed "The Dogpatch" and was cryptically called site X. The plant, itself, was labeled K-25. It is located some thirty miles from Knoxville and is the world's largest single factory under one roof. Shaped in the form of a giant U with sides one mile long this mammoth four-story plant was covered by sixty acres of roofing. The total plant with some seventy auxiliary structures sprawled over an area of six hundred acres. It was built by the Kellex Corporation, a specially created subsidiary of the M. W. Kellog Company. When the K-25 plant was first operated in 1944 it took 11,000 workers to operate and maintain this continuous flow process. Many of these employees were completely in the dark about the nature of the work and they must have had their misgivings about such a huge plant which took so much power, was so cantankerous in operation, and which produced no visible product. Some probably dismissed the whole thing as a New Deal rathole development.

Other types of separation plants were also built at the Oak Ridge site but we need not go into the ancient history of these plants. All in all the separation plants cost approximately $800 million and at peak activity some 75,000 people crowded into the town of Oak Ridge which mushroomed from almost zero population to become the third largest city in Tennessee. The vastness of the atomic industry built at Oak Ridge was to make this newly born town famous the world over. Its very name was to become synonymous with atomic energy. Besides being the home of the gigantic diffusion plant Oak Ridge also was the site for a smaller but no less important plant. This was the pilot plant for the production of plutonium. However, this takes us a little too swiftly into the second story of the Manhattan Project. To begin properly we must go back to 1942 to what we may call the Plutonium Project.

To understand just what plutonium is and how it is made let us reflect back on the experiments which Fermi carried out in Italy when he first bombarded uranium with neutrons. He reasoned that if he could make a neutron stick inside an atom of uranium he might convert it into an atom of a new element. Uranium being element No. 92, Fermi advanced the hypothesis that element No. 93 might be formed by this neutron bombardment. We know now that what Fermi and his colleagues actually found was not a new element but actually the splitting of the uranium atom. But undoubtedly a very tiny amount of element 93 must also have been formed in the sample of uranium. This new element was not identified, however, until 1940 when two American scientists Edwin McMillan and Philip Abelson isolated enough of it to permit analysis.

In the Oak Ridge diffusion process it is the U-235 which is the all-important isotope, U-238 being the unwanted material. When we consider the production of plutonium it is the U-238 which plays the key role. Neutrons striking a sample of uranium may cause fission in the U-235 or they may be captured by the U-238 in which case the latter does not usually fission. Instead the U-238 swallows up the neutron and becomes a new isotope of uranium, namely U-239. The newly created U-239 is very unstable and every twenty-three minutes half of it disintegrates to form an isotope of element 93. To this element we give the name neptunium after the planet Neptune which lies beyond Uranus in our solar system. The chemical symbol is Np and since the isotope has number 239 we will be sophisticated and refer to it as Np-239. Things do not stop with Np-239 for it, like U-239, is unstable. Every 2.3 days it is found that half of it disappears to form still another isotope of a new element called plutonium. This element number 94 gets its name from the planet Pluto, the next neighbor of Neptune, and bears the undignified chemical symbol Pu. Appropriately enough, the name is also that for the god of the underworld, for Pu-239 is a close relative of U-235 in that it fissions in the same way. Thus both these isotopes,

U-235 which must be painfully extracted from uranium and Pu-239 which is synthesized by neutron annexation in U-238, are rivals as prime ingredients for an A-bomb.

Physicists made one of the most daring scientific forays when they dreamed that it would someday be possible to manufacture plutonium in quantities sufficient for an A-bomb. In principle all you had to do was to bombard U-238 (ordinary or natural uranium would do very nicely since it is 99.3 per cent pure U-238 and 0.7 per cent U-235) with neutrons. But where would one get the neutrons? The puny radium-beryllium source would never make enough plutonium to see in a high-power microscope. Even giant cyclotrons which could produce neutrons were too weak to ever make more than pinhead quantities of the new element. Atomic scientists dreamed up a very fancy and almost impossible plan. The scheme was daring but simple in concept. Briefly, it envisaged using the neutrons released in the fission of the small fraction of U-235 in uranium. The idea was to make a nuclear machine called a "pile" or "reactor" in which one would achieve a controlled chain reaction rather than a runaway reaction such as contemplated for the A-bomb. With this nuclear reactor the fissions from U-235 would produce neutrons over and above those needed to keep the chain reaction perking along. These excess neutrons would be absorbed in rods of U-238 and thus converted into plutonium.

Before going any further it may be well to pause and ask, "Isn't this the long way home? Why go to all the trouble of making Pu-239 this way when you could strip U-235 off from its partner U-238?" The answer involves a pair of arguments. First, it was not certain that the U-235 diffusion plants would pay off in time. Second, since the plutonium was a different element from uranium it could be chemically separated from the uranium and might on the whole be a much better way to make a bomb material. For these reasons and also because in the long run the controlled chain reaction promised to provide man with a potent source of power the Manhattan Project launched a vigorous Plutonium Project with Nobel prizewinner Arthur H. Compton as its leader.

Unlike the U-235 separation process which was a long hard pull with no big milestones to mark its progress, the plutonium process had spectacular highlights. The first of these really marks the beginning of the Atomic Age. On December 2, 1942, slightly under one year after Pearl Harbor and the all-out decision on the A-bomb, the first nuclear chain reaction was produced. Experiments which had been carried out at Columbia University indicated that a design of graphite carbon blocks intermingled with lumps of uranium looked promising for attaining a chain reaction. Research work on the diffusion process was centered at Columbia so it was decided to move the chain reaction work to Chicago. There on the campus of the University of Chicago a galaxy of famous scientists were assembled to put together the first atomic pile. As a ruse to deceive too inquisitive neighbors the title of "Metallurgical Laboratory" was selected.

Wherever there was any available space in campus buildings this new project poured personnel and equipment. Soon the expanding laboratory pushed beyond the bounds of the campus and spewed across the famous Midway where Chicago's World's Fair was held. An abandoned brewery was appropriated and dubbed "Site B." This, mind you, was right in the middle of the residential South Side and the procession of trucks pulling up to this plant every day excited much local gossip, the more so because no one ever saw a truck take anything away. I can vouch for these rumors for I lived in an apartment house directly adjoining Site B and the speculation of my neighbors was often laugh-provoking. When questioned about what I did in this building (which I was known to enter frequently) my stock reply was "I'm really not sure what we're doing."

One site into which the laboratory overflowed has become world-famous. Today, a small metal plaque outside the squash courts of the West Stands at the University of Chicago athletic field marks the place where the world's first chain reaction was achieved. There in an abandoned squash court a not very imposing pile of graphite blocks was stacked up layer upon layer. In alternate layers, and in carefully calculated positions, there were imbedded vessels of uranium. The latter was mostly in metallic form and was, of course, natural uranium as it comes from the ore refinery, not the kind that was later produced at Oak Ridge. Running right into the center of this pile were several rods or strips of cadmium, an element often used in protective plating of metal. These were the "control rods" and they constituted the only moving parts of this silent machine. When finally the last layer of the shiny, almost greasy, graphite blocks had been stacked up the machine was ready for testing. As top scientists like Compton, Fermi, Wigner, and others looked on the control rod was slowly withdrawn from the pile. A neutron counter recorded the increase in the number of neutrons produced by the machine and all eyes were glued on this instrument. Slowly at first and then more rapidly the neutrons increased in abundance until finally the frenzied recording of the counter told the scientists that a nuclear chain reaction had been attained. The scene was a dramatic one, not quite as supercharged as the Hollywood version in the film *The Beginning or the End* but still highly dramatic as things in science go. A bottle of rare Italian wine was broken out and the occasion was duly marked with ceremony but with little pomp.

Scientists were elated with their initial success. Now they could proceed to the larger task of designing a high-power pile, one which would be capable of generating vast quantities of neutrons every second so that these could in turn be used to convert U-238 into Pu-239. The first pile did not produce enough energy to light even a small electric lamp but it signaled the opening of the Atomic Age for now the chain reaction was a fact not a theory. We shall not pause at this time to describe how the chain reactor works for we shall have much more to say about this point later on.

Although the experiment in the squash court marked the beginning of the Atomic Age it was at the time known only to a relatively few scientists. The stands on the University football field were under constant armed guard and only scientists with proper credentials and a photographic pass were admitted. This was true in general. One spring day I proved the exception to the rule. I had been pursuing my own nonsecret research studying cosmic rays with equipment housed in the press box atop Stagg Field stadium. One day while lugging down a Geiger counter outfit I took a short cut and soon found myself inside the stands amid other white-jacketed men. Apparently because I looked right at home with jacket and Geiger counter I was not challenged by the guards and roamed around for a while. Upon leaving the site a guard asked for my pass. Shortly after the hubbub died down I "officially" joined the project.

The first Chicago pile did not produce any plutonium. Small amounts of the new element were badly needed if the huge chemical plants for separating it from uranium were to be properly designed. To obtain token amounts of it cyclotrons were run overtime at the University of California and also at Washington University in St. Louis. Neutrons from these machines were used to bombard several hundred pounds of a uranium compound and by the end of 1942 the first weighable amounts of the element were produced. This was not enough to be weighed on a butcher's scale; in fact, the total amount of plutonium weighed about one hundred times less than the weight of a postage stamp. Yet it was with such an insignificant pinpoint of the new element that chemical processes were worked out.

Scientists then set to work to make a bigger pile, one which would produce larger amounts of plutonium and at the same time serve as a pilot plant for the full-scale production plants which were to produce plutonium for the bomb. This intermediate nuclear reactor was built at Oak Ridge during 1943 and it is still in use today. It furnished valuable guidance for the solution of problems encountered in dealing with the huge plutonium production piles which we shall now discuss.

With the success of the chain reaction great stress was then placed on the production of plutonium. No time could be spared to wait for the operation of the pilot plant at Oak Ridge. Plans were rushed to completion to build full-scale reactors. At a time when there were less than postage-stamp amounts of the final product of these proposed plants the most grandiose and detailed plans were drawn. E. I. Du Pont de Nemours and Company was selected for the job. General Groves personally decided against locating the plants at Oak Ridge and instead selected a remote site in the state of Washington. There where the mighty Columbia River joins with the Yakima River to flow to the Pacific a huge reservation of some 620 square miles was staked out. This is an area more than half the size of the state of Rhode Island. Only two small towns, Hanford and Richland, interrupted the dry, almost desertlike, stretch of territory. Machines bit into this powdery soil in the early spring of 1943 and soon 60,000 people thronged the temporary construction town at Hanford and 15,000 more swelled the town of Richland.

Building the Hanford plants turned out to be a task which often left Du Pont engineers and construction experts in a bewildered daze. On every side there were problems which had never been faced before in the construction of any plant. Some, the scientists flatly admitted, had no predictable solution. You had to build it and find out if it would work. In other cases, when pressed for answers, the scientists calmly replied that solutions would be forthcoming in a few weeks or a few months. But if to the engineers the scientists appeared calm and confident, among themselves the atomic experts had their own doubts. Nobel prize winners worried over such new problems as "What would happen to the graphite in the pile after it was exposed to neutrons for several months?" Some experts predicted that the continual bombardment of the graphite would change its structure until one day it would suddenly release its stored up energy and that would spell disaster for Hanford. Others said that this might happen but it was a chance you had to take. Far from being reckless, scientists tried to make sure in advance that nothing would go wrong. In this case they hoped for the best and resolved to keep a careful check on the pile. So the work went on. Designs were changed at the last minute much to the consternation of Du Pont engineers who shuttled back and forth from Chicago where the scientists evolved the Hanford plans.

A tribute to the scientists, to the Du Pont Company and to the U. S. Army engineers was the fact that in September of 1944 the first of the big Hanford piles was started up. This was the first of three such plants to be completed before the end of the year.

They were essentially the same in design. Each was a huge undertaking as can be seen from the fact that the water required to cool one pile was about the same as that used by the city of Toledo. The Columbia River was an excellent source of pure cold water to run through the piles and remove heat from them. Fed in under pressure and directed through the structure in aluminum tubes the water was heated up and then shortly thereafter discharged into the river. Precautions were taken to make sure that none of this discharge water became contaminated with radioactivity so that it might be a hazard to fish or to humans.

Handling and chemically processing the uranium after it had been cooked in the pile long enough to accumulate recoverable amounts of plutonium was a task as formidable as the design and building of the piles, themselves. Furthermore, these techniques and processes had to be designed on the basis of experiments with postage-stamp amounts of plutonium. Here the chemists of the Metallurgical Laboratory and of Oak Ridge did a superb job. Not the least of their worries was the development of the chemical processes to win the plutonium from the uranium rods. All chemical operations with these extremely radioactive metal slugs had to be carried out by remote control. The scheme devised to deal with uranium slugs so "hot" that they had to be covered up with twenty feet of water when first pushed out of the Hanford pile was this. First, the slugs were allowed to "cool" that is, die out in radioactivity by waiting for two months or so before attempting to do anything with them. During this cooling-off period the uranium slugs with their small fraction of plutonium lay in buckets under water. In two months the split halves of all the uranium atoms which had fissioned while in the pile decayed radioactively so that the radioactive hazard was very significantly reduced. Then the metal slugs were chemically treated so that their aluminum jackets came off. Thereupon a series of chemical processes separated the plutonium from the mass of uranium. All of these operations took place in a huge concrete "canyon" where thick concrete walls protected personnel. [Enough concrete went into one canyon to pave a highway thirty miles long.] Everything was handled by remote control through ingenious instruments which were made specifically for the task.

The final product, plutonium, was then purified to remove any traces of radioactivity and it was temporarily stored in small stainless steel spill-proof vessels which went into a guarded vault. No plans had been made to do anything with the vast quantities of uranium solution left over from the chemical plant so it was stored in huge tanks, popularly called the General's tanks. There the radioactive solution, some millions of gallons, was stored until after the war pending bright ideas as to what could be done about it. The plutonium, however, did not long remain in the state of Washington. It was secretly transported by the Army to a secret laboratory which had been built in the hills about thirty-five miles from Santa Fe, New Mexico. We now arrive at the third of our three stories about the Manhattan Project—the actual development of the atomic bomb.

It took a delicate blend of theory and experiment to evolve finally the designs for a mechanism to produce an atomic explosion. The master blender was Dr. J. Robert Oppenheimer. In the summer of 1942 he gathered together a small group of theoreticians at the University of Chicago and drew up estimates of the feasibility of the A-bomb. On paper the bomb looked feasible although it was still too early to figure out how much U-235 or Pu-239 would be required in the weapon or "gadget" as the bomb became known to most physicists. Just about the time that ground was being broken at Hanford, a site for the weapons laboratory was set up on a mesa in New Mexico. It could be reached mainly by a dangerous winding road which scared some people more than the thought that an atomic experiment might get out of hand. The location appealed to the Army for the isolation seemed to insure security. No one at that time knew that within the barbed wire fences of Los Alamos the Soviets were to have their informers.

Within a year the youthful director of the laboratory, Dr. Oppenheimer, had attracted the best scientific brains in the country—at least all that could be spared from other projects. As soon as scientists had cracked the toughest phases of the Hanford problem they were assigned to Los Alamos. Work went on in high gear all through 1944 and was then stepped up to a feverish pace in the spring of 1945 when it became evident that soon the Oak Ridge and Hanford plants would produce enough fissionable material for an A-bomb test. By this time the bomb experts had pinned down the critical size of a sphere of U-235 or Pu-239, *i.e.*, the amount needed to achieve the chain reaction. The big problem was finding some way to bring together an over-critical amount of the material so that it would fission and produce an atomic explosion. Besides bringing the mass of U-235 or Pu-239 together quickly, or making an "assembly" to use the technical jargon, some arrangement had to be made to keep the whole thing together long enough so that enough fissions would occur to make the whole business practicable. "Long enough" was roughly one-millionth of a second. Obviously, assembling an A-bomb was tricky business and required neat timing if all was to go well.

Two techniques were dreamed up to make an A-bomb work. The first was a brute force method in which the gadget is simply a gun. However, it's a rather unusual gun for it has no open end.

It works in the following way. At one end of the massive gun barrel is a target of U-235 while at the other end is a projectile of the same material. Separated by the length of the barrel the two pieces of U-235 are below the critical point and no chain reaction takes place. However, when one is fired at the other by means of an explosive propellent the two fuse together and form an overcritical mass. A chain reaction takes place instantly and keeps going until the heat generated by the fissions blows the whole mass apart. This, then, is an atomic explosion. The heavy gun barrel serves as a tamper to keep the chain reaction from blowing itself apart too soon and wasting the valuable material.

The other gadget design is far trickier and much more sophisticated. It is the design which was used in the A-bomb exploded over Nagasaki. According to David Greenglass, a former Army sergeant at Los Alamos, the principle of this gadget was that of *implosion*. This was a new word when first introduced into the testimony of David Greenglass at the atomic espionage hearings in 1951 when he stood trial for giving atomic secrets to the Russians. Accounts published in the *New York Times* of March 12, 1951 state that implosion "used in reference to the atomic bomb refers to a basic concept of the missile. The principle is that of a guided explosion focused inward. The implosion in the bomb described in court is created by the explosion of lenses. The term lens is not used in its usual meaning of a curved piece of glass, but refers to a curve-shaped high explosive. Thirty-six of these lenses surround the fusible material that is the core of the bomb, and their simultaneous explosion with its force directed inward creates the necessary stimulus to set off the chain reaction and the resulting explosion." This in essence was the design of the gadget which experts at Los Alamos called the "Fat Man."

Work on perfecting the gadget reached its peak in 1945 and, although many refinements could still be made, the weapons experts were ready to test the first bomb as soon as enough material arrived from Oak Ridge and Hanford. This point, namely that the A-bomb mechanism was ready prior to the time when the U-235 or Pu-239 was ready, is something to bear in mind in considering how much time Dr. Fuchs saved the Soviets. We shall return to this point in the chapter on secrecy; for the moment we emphasize that the time required for producing the bomb material was the determining factor in our race to get the bomb. Early in the summer of 1945 enough plutonium was shipped in from Hanford for the metallurgists at Los Alamos to fabricate the core of an A-bomb. The world's first atomic weapon was ready for test.

There is no need for describing again the drama of this first atomic explosion which took place in the desert at Alamogordo. The story of how the desert was illuminated with the new force drawn from the atom has been told many times. News of the successful test was speeded to President Truman who received it at Potsdam where he was conferring with Winston Churchill and Joseph Stalin. According to an eyewitness, President Truman thereafter conferred with his advisers and decided to let Stalin in on the secret. Striding to one end of the conference hall he broke the news to Stalin. Rather than producing a profound effect on the Soviet leader the news was received quite passively; this, Truman later stated, he felt was to be explained by Stalin's inability to comprehend the meaning of the news. We know now that Stalin had been kept well informed of our progress on the A-bomb.

One point about the first atomic explosion is worth adding. It has often been stated that the scientists did not know beforehand whether the A-bomb would work. However, to most of the top scientists it was not a question of whether it would work but how well. This is reflected in a memorandum submitted to President Truman on April 25, 1945, the first paragraph of which reads: "Within four months we shall in all probability have completed the most terrible weapon ever known in human history, one bomb of which could destroy a whole city." Thus, our President had time to think over the use of this as yet untried weapon. His decision to use it was not precipitous but was based upon the considered advice of top scientists and government officials. Germany had been defeated but in the Pacific the Japanese still posed a serious military threat to the United States. Incidentally, a special investigative group of scientists had dashed into Germany following hard upon the heels of our troops to discover how far the Germans had gotten in their atomic project. Then, and only then, did we realize that the Germans had not gotten to first base in their work. Our intelligence information had been completely misleading. As regards the atomic activities of the Japs there was little worry that we were in an atomic arms race. The big problem in making the decision to use the bomb again hinged upon intelligence information, this time about the Japanese will to continue the war.

By the spring of 1945 it had already been decided that the home islands of Japan were to be invaded by a huge American task force. The date finally agreed upon was November 15, 1945. Behind the scenes there were some bitter arguments about this decision and some Air Corps officers maintained that their chief, General Hap Arnold, sold them out when he agreed to this invasion thereby admitting that air bombardment of Japan could not win the war. These officers maintain even today that in the strategic bombardment of Japan the Air Corps had a perfect textbook military problem. Photo reconnaissance showed that General LeMay's B-29s were sapping the life blood of the home islands with continued attacks upon the main cities. General LeMay, himself, was convinced that the Japs could not hold up much longer under this savage rain of fire and high explosives. In terms of the damage which an A-bomb could do the B-29s were delivering incendiaries and T.N.T bombs equivalent to one A-bomb every two to three days. Later, the official findings of the U. S. Strategic Bombing Survey in Japan were to agree with the Air Corps contention that Japan could have been knocked out by continuation of the air attack.

This view, however, was not shared by the Army or by General Marshall. The principal reason why the A-bomb was used was that it seemed the only alternative to the planned invasion. President Truman has recorded: "General Marshall said in Potsdam that if the bomb worked we would save a quarter of a million American lives and probably save millions of Japanese." One can talk until doomsday about the wisdom of the American decision to use the bomb but the unalterable fact is that we did decide to employ this new weapon in our war against Japan.

The decision made, it was a question of rounding up all the available U-235 and Pu-239 and converting it into bombs. Even though the tanks at Oak Ridge were drained and the Hanford works were pushed to the limit there wasn't very much fissionable material on hand; only enough for two or three bombs. But military authorities took the gamble and the bombs were readied for use in the Pacific where specially trained B-29 crews at Tinian awaited the order to make the first atomic air strike. This period during the last few days of July and the first few in August were deeply impressed on my memory. I had been commuting between Los Alamos and the Chicago laboratory and knew that the bomb would be dropped during the first week in August, the exact date depending upon the weather. To my knowledge the only other person in Chicago who was also aware of this momentous impending event was the Project leader A. H. Compton. It was with tense expectation that I tuned in my radio for the midnight news flashes during the first days of August. Around me lay the sprawling metropolis of Chicago unaware of the turn which history was to take and across the Pacific was a smaller city equally unaware.

Then came August 6, 1945, and the atomic concussion which rocked Hiroshima and reverberated around the world. A single plane with a single bomb had virtually destroyed an entire city. A few days later came the second atomic blast, this time a more powerful one. Underneath its unleashed fury lay the devastated city of Nagasaki. Then on August 15, 1945, the newspapers proclaimed that "THE GREAT WAR ENDS." Such was the quick succession of events which followed the first military use of an atomic bomb.

Starting the day before Pearl Harbor and ending in midsummer of 1945 two and one-half years of feverish work had converted atomic energy into a crucial factor in world affairs. In looking back over the highlights of the all-important plutonium work and the weapons research at Los Alamos, it should be understood that the contributions of foreign-born scientists were of paramount importance. Time and time again the genius of Fermi, Wigner, Bethe, or a dozen other men provided the critical judgment which spelled success for the project. In retrospect it is discomfiting to imagine how the bomb project would have proceeded had it not been for the initiative and genius of these scientific refugees. Had we then in effect certain concepts of security which enshackle the nation today one wonders if there would have been a Nagasaki, for the A-bomb was in principle an importation from Europe.

With the ending of the war the European ancestry of the atomic bomb was promptly forgotten especially by the legislators who presumably never knew the lineage anyway. The United States erected security barriers to prevent the interchange of information with other nations, even with those who helped us so much during the war. As we shall see in dealing with the entire secrecy and security question this policy did not and could not keep the Soviets from getting the A-bomb; nor was Dr. Fuchs necessary for the Soviet success in building their own Oak Ridges and Hanfords. The biggest secret of all was revealed to the world in the ecliptic explosion which blotted out the sun that a moment before had been shining on the city of Hiroshima. That was that an A-bomb was possible and that it worked.

4

POSTWAR DEVELOPMENT

THE war was over. Gone was the urgency for the scientists to toil behind the barbed-wire encirclements of secret laboratories. In droves scientists left the Manhattan Project to return to the less hectic and unfettered atmosphere of the college campus. Far from feeling proud of their wartime accomplishment in atomic energy, despite the public adulation which generally placed science on a lofty pedestal, many scientists felt almost a sense of guilt about having helped to bring into the world what seemed to be an uncontrollable force.

But while the bomb makers deserted the atomic project they did not forget the problems which the atom had created. Even before the detonation of the first bomb a number of them had begun to ponder how the new force could be put to work for man's benefit. Little work had been done on this phase of atomic energy due to the necessity for winning the war but the development of the Hanford production plants paved the way for making nuclear power plants and ushering in the age of atomic power. The atom, scientists reasoned, would eventually assume a very large role in the affairs of men. They therefore determined to campaign for civilian control of atomic energy in the United States.

Atomic scientists by the score invaded Washington and set up the first scientific lobby in the nation's history. These men were not skilled in the art of applying pressure to Congressmen and to influential bigwigs in the nation's capital. They were not even knit into a closely co-ordinated group with a well-defined strategy. But they were effective. Perhaps, because of their naïveté or perhaps in spite of their bumbling and highly unorthodox frontal attack they were able to see the right people and say some of the right things. During this invasion the city of Washington witnessed some strange scenes. Long-haired legislators were to be seen closeted with earnest young scientists, some with crew-cuts. Newspapers featured a photograph showing a boyish-appearing scientist, chalk in hand, using a blackboard to illustrate to a senator the meaning of $E = mc^2$.

General Leslie Groves to many a scientist symbolized the evil of military control and a few singled out the General for rather bitter criticism. At the time the General did not endear himself to the scientists by the speeches he was making around the country and by the political maneuvers he was reputed to be practicing on Capitol Hill. Some physicists, feeling that he was claiming more than a fair share of credit for making the A-bomb, jibed at him with the remark that his speeches were of the "I did it alone" flavor. This was rather unfortunate for there was enough credit for everyone. Furthermore, the General was having his own

(51)

troubles in the Pentagon where a number of star-wearing officers were seeking to prepare a bed of thorns for him. Contrary to what was generally believed there was no widely supported military "plot" to keep the heavy military fist clamped down on atomic energy. However, it was true that there was a faction that opposed civilian control of atomic energy.

Early in October, 1945, President Truman sent a message to the Congress urging that legislation be enacted for the development of atomic energy. A single paragraph from this message expresses the sanguine hopes for atomic energy which then prevailed:

The discovery of the means of releasing atomic energy began a new era in the history of civilization. The scientific and industrial knowledge upon which this discovery rests does not relate merely to another weapon. It may some day prove to be more revolutionary in the development of human society than the invention of the wheel, the use of metals, or the steam or internal combustion engine.

There was widespread optimism about this new force, and on the basis of their demonstrated success in wartime the scientists had reason to be self-assured about their ability to convert atomic energy into a great national asset. This rosy view of the peacetime atom was to expand during the next several years.

In contrast with all the talk about doing things with atomic energy the atomic project, itself, entered a period of the doldrums. A year and a half was to elapse before civilian control of the project was established. During this period atomic energy suffered a severe hiatus. Very little new research was started and bomb production inched along. The whole atomic program marked time while Congress debated the merits of several different bills. The May-Johnson bill providing for greater military control was one which invoked the opposition of many scientists, and due to their objections the legislation was not passed. The Senate thereupon organized a special committee on atomic energy under the chairmanship of Senator Brien McMahon, the late Democratic senator from Connecticut. McMahon was from then, until his untimely death, to be known as Mr. Atom on Capitol Hill for he closely associated himself and his career with atomic developments. Under his direction the special committee organized a series of hearings. Top scientists, engineers, and executives were called in to testify on every phase of the atomic problem. These hearings, which appeared in printed form throughout 1945 and 1946, still form a gold mine of information for the serious student of atomic energy, containing as they do testimony which appears nowhere else in the atomic literature. Here one finds every conceivable topic discussed in question and answer form, the senators asking the questions and the civilian and military experts providing the answers. Some of the answers are so enlightening that in terms of today's security regulations they would not be permitted to be released to the public.

Here are some of the questions which the senators asked of their witnesses: How difficult had it been to make the A-bomb? When would other countries have the bomb? Was there any defense against the bomb? What atomic secrets did we have? Could we keep them? Were we giving away too much information? What were the peacetime benefits of atomic energy?

The answers varied from witness to witness. After rereading over 1,000 pages of the original testimony the writer was impressed with the accuracy of many of the replies. True, many of the witnesses overstressed the difficulty of making an A-bomb but this was only natural. Almost everyone guessed wrong on when Russia would have the bomb. Dr. Irving Langmuir of the

General Electric Company, however, was uncannily correct in predicting: "I believe that the Russians will produce their first atomic bombs in about three years." Two things deserve comment in qualifying Dr. Langmuir as a witness; first, he had only trivial contact with our own bomb work and could therefore view it dispassionately, and, second, he had made a postwar trip to Russia—something no other witness appearing before the committee had done. It is to be hoped that the next sentence in Dr. Langmuir's testimony is less prophetic than the one just quoted: "Thereafter, however, there is a definite possibility that the Russians might accumulate bombs at a faster rate than we do."

All in all it may be stated that the legislators were deeply impressed with the magnitude of the atomic problem and they deliberated over it very carefully. They queried witness after witness on topics ranging from the effects of the Hiroshima bomb to whether uranium would compete with coal as an energy source. As legislators accustomed to being bludgeoned by high-pressure lobbies they must have wondered at the sanity of the scientists for they did not cohere as a solid front. Very often two distinguished scientists would present opposing testimony on the same issue—a highly unorthodox procedure for lobbyists. The scientists, however, cared little for convention. Their sole objective was to secure civilian control of atomic energy and acceptable regulations so that atomic research and development would prosper in this country. Their efforts were crowned with success for they convinced a majority of the Congressmen of their sincerity and of the soundness of their proposals for promoting the utilization of atomic energy.

In the winter of 1945-46 Senator Brien McMahon introduced a bill to deal with atomic energy and by early summer it had weathered Congressional debate and on August 1, 1946, was made a law of the land, thereafter being known by either of three titles—the McMahon Act, the Atomic Energy Act of 1946, or Public Law 585. As contained in the first paragraph of this act, the declared policy was:

Accordingly, it is hereby declared to be the policy of the people of the United States that, subject at all times to the paramount objective of assuring the common defense and security, the development and utilization of atomic energy shall, so far as practicable, be directed toward improving the public welfare, increasing the standard of living, strengthening free competition in private enterprise, and promoting world peace.

This piece of legislation has been called the most radical law of the land. It established an Atomic Energy Commission, consisting of a chairman and four other civilian members, and entrusted them with sweeping powers. As an example of these unprecedented powers we need only point to the mandatory monopoly which the Commission was instructed to assume over all facilities for the production of fissionable material. The new agency took over all the capital investments of the Manhattan Project—these alone totaling $1.3 billion. Furthermore, the Atomic Energy Commission was to own all fissionable material in the land. Thus the AEC became the most total monopoly in the history of the United States. And like all monopolies this one was destined to have serious disadvantages although they did not become apparent immediately.

Two further clauses in the Atomic Energy Act are worthy of specific mention. One reserved for the President the right to transfer bombs or bomb material from the AEC to the armed forces. This stipulation was inserted in the act presumably to insure against any impetuous A-bomb use by the military. Another had to do with the dissemination of atomic energy data and here the legislation told the Commission to go in two directions at the same time. On one hand it warned the agency against giving away restricted data, stipulating that "there shall be no exchange of information with other nations with respect to the use of atomic energy for industrial purposes." On the other hand it urged that dissemination of data "should be permitted and encouraged so as to provide that free interchange of ideas and criticisms which is essential to scientific progress."

When it came to the sore point of how the military should engage in atomic activities the McMahon Act made two allowance for military participation in the work of the Atomic Energy Commission. First, it established with the AEC a Division of Military Application. Second, it also set up a Military Liaison Committee consisting of representatives of the armed services. This committee was to advise and consult with the AEC on military applications of atomic energy. It is important to repeat here that on the five-man Commission there were no active duty military men so that from a policy-making standpoint the military Liaison Committee was as close as the military could get to the atomic agency. Before passage of the McMahon Act, Secretary of the Navy Forrestal had vigorously protested excluding military representatives from the Commission stating that "I do feel most strongly that the military departments of the government should have a voice in this Commission." In theory this committee should have been able to function effectively but in practice the three services used the committee as a sort of local Washington battleground for settling their differences. I was assigned to this committee and I had many an opportunity to observe the footwork of the generals and admirals. Sometimes I was so dismayed by their antics that I closed my eyes and imagined that it was merely a transitory scene from Gilbert and Sullivan. Today the committee functions more smoothly than in its first several years mostly because the lion's share of the work being done by the AEC is strictly military and each service is essentially getting everything it wants.

To insure that the Commission would be properly advised on matters scientific the Congress specified that there should be a General Advisory Committee with nine civilian members appointed by the President. Highly qualified scientists were appointed by President Truman who selected J. Robert Oppenheimer as chairman and surrounded him with such stellar personalities as James B. Conant, Enrico Fermi, I. I. Rabi, Lee duBridge, and Glenn T. Seaborg. The committee included a number of Nobel prize winners and by and large it was packed with scientists. The too scientific attitude of the advisory committee might well have been tempered by adding to it the sound judgment of engineers and executives, for as it turned out many of the staggering problems which confronted the Commission and on which it desperately needed guidance were of an engineering or business nature even more than they were scientific or technical.

Finally, the Atomic Energy Act established one more committee. This was the Joint Congressional Committee on Atomic Energy. After all of its long deliberations on the atom the Congress was reluctant to entrust such a mighty force to a government agency without setting up some sort of Congressional watchdog group. And a very diligent watchdog it turned out to be.

At midnight on the last day of 1946 the famous Manhattan Project ceased to exist. All of its assets were turned over to the new civilian Atomic Energy Commission. The President had designated David E. Lilienthal, the former head of TVA to be the AEC chairman. The other commissioners were Dr. Robert F. Bacher, a nuclear physicist; Sumner T. Pike, a retired executive; Lewis L. Strauss, an admiral on the reserve list, and William W. Waymack, a former newspaperman. Then began the Senate hearings on the confirmation of these appointments. Beginning late in January they dragged through February and extended in March as aging Senator Kenneth McKellar, a bitter foe of Lilienthal and TVA, sought to disqualify the President's choice for the AEC chairmanship.

Lilienthal was subjected to a grueling cross fire of barbed questions. Many of these were so irrelevant that they would have tried the patience of a saint. Something of the flavor of the cross-examination is communicated by quoting a single accusatory question hurled at the witness by the Senator from Tennessee:

Senator McKellar: Did it not seem remarkable to you, who have never been an engineer, who knew nothing in the world about the splitting of the atom or about atomic energy and its discovery, that the President should not reappoint General Groves, who was an engineer, and who had made this greatest discovery of all time? That he should turn to you, now, one who is not an engineer, knowing nothing in the world about it, and appoint you as head of this Commission? Was that not a little striking to you? It was to me. I will say that.

The Senator said that and many other things besides, ranging from an indictment of the TVA as a "hotbed of communism" to thinly veiled assertions that it would not be safe to give our biggest secret to the care of one Mr. Lilienthal. The hearings appeared later in printed form, totaling 951 pages of testimony and evidence. Yet the first AEC chairman endured the endless monotony of the inquisition and emerged seemingly triumphant, confirmed to be helmsman of the atomic program in this country.

But in retrospect Lilienthal did not emerge unscathed; his was something of a Pyrrhic victory. When the new chairman rolled up his sleeves to tackle the tough problems confronting the AEC he did so as a political target. Thereafter his actions and those of the AEC were to be scrutinized from Capitol Hill. The slightest chink that appeared in his armor would most certainly be the thrusting point for a Congressional investigation. Under these conditions it was not surprising that the newly created agency should proceed with caution and should be invested with deep conservatism. Those under Lilienthal moved slowly lest precipitous actions should incur failure and bring down on the AEC the wrath of McKellar and his colleagues. Thus it was that a true liberal came to head up an organization which moved with all the discretion and slowness of a century-old government bureau.

Inventory of the business which the AEC inherited from the Manhattan Project soon convinced the commissioners that the atomic project was at its lowest ebb. The huge plutonium production plants along the Columbia River were in sad need of repair or replacement. There was a need to analyze all the various types of plants at Oak Ridge and decide which one or ones should be counted upon to bear the brunt of producing U-235; then the plants had to be refurbished and made to turn out the enriched uranium more economically. Somehow or other the critically important Los Alamos weapons laboratory had to be resuscitated and brought to work on new weapon designs to use uranium and plutonium more efficiently. Throughout the research centers of the AEC new scientific personnel had to be recruited to replace the scientists who had returned to their prewar pursuits. Those who remained had low morale and there was a critical need for formulating a dynamic program to keep up the work of those within the AEC laboratories.

Yet even as the AEC was completing its inventory and figuring out ways and means to put things in shape, the world picture was steadily darkening. And as international relations between the United States and the Soviet Union deteriorated more and more public figures began to regard the A-bomb as a big stick to deter the Russians from aggressing. In the face of this situation the military placed demands upon the Atomic Energy Commission which impressed upon the latter a program which was at least 90 per cent military in its make-up. The Commission reacted to pressure from the Pentagon and Capitol Hill by undertaking the first of a series of postwar expansions which were ultimately to total over $6 billion for capital outlays to build new plants and furnish them with equipment. So vast was the program to become that ultimately about $1 billion per year were to be required just for operating expenses.

Before describing this expansion program it may be well to comment upon its general nature. By and large the expansion concentrated upon the duplication of wartime facilities. One may either assume that these were so good that they needed no improvement or that there was a reluctance within the atomic agency to put its blue chips on new developments. It is difficult to conceive of anything in science so well planned that the first model could not bear extensive revision. I believe that the unwillingness of the AEC to take chances with new developments to replace wartime methods of producing U-235 and Pu-239 stemmed from the sensitivity which it developed to the brooding eye of the "Watchdog Committee" in the Congress.

The postwar atomic expansion came in three stages so far as Congressional appropriations are concerned but in the building of plants there was no sharp line of demarcation between the construction activities. The first stage of expansion was authorized late in 1947, and by mid-1948 it was in full swing with rowdy gangs of construction workers thronging the atomic sites. Some 15,000 men were hired in the state of Washington to construct new plutonium-producing reactors similar to those built during the war. At first it was thought that the wartime plants could not be rehabilitated and would have to be shut down but methods were worked out to keep them in operation. Two more powerful nuclear reactors were added to the three already on the banks of the Columbia River. Dr. L. N. Ridenour publicly estimated that the latter ran at a power level of "around a million kilowatts" so that with the additions a tremendous quantity of power was generated along the Columbia but not a single kilowatt was used for power. It simply heated up the chilly waters of that mighty river.

In the first phase of the expansion program a policy decision had to be made on which type of separation process should be backed at the Oak Ridge site. Careful evaluation of the competing processes led to the decision that the gaseous diffusion plant of the K-25 type was the best bet. Accordingly the Y-12 electromagnetic separation plant in which the government had sunk $350 million in cash and an equal quantity in silver bullion (the latter being borrowed from Fort Knox to serve as an electrical conductor in place of hard-to-get-copper) was shelved. A new series of K-plants was started at the Oak Ridge site using a plant design which proved to be somewhat more efficient than the wartime one.

When Congress approved a second large appropriation for atomic expansion it was decided that there were too many "atomic eggs" in two baskets so in the interests of national security as well as to insure more adequate power supply two new atomic sites were located.

A new Oak Ridge was slated for construction near Paducah,

Kentucky, and about $500 million were allocated to building new diffusion plants at this site. These diffusion plants require extremely large amounts of power and to supply the electrical energy for the new site a new organization called Electric Energy, Inc., together with TVA, was asked to supply 960,000 kilowatts of electrical power. An almost identical amount of power was also needed for the previously indicated expansion at Oak Ridge.

The other new atomic site was selected to be near Aiken, South Carolina, on the banks of the Savannah River. Popularly known as the H-bomb plant the new facility is in reality a dual purpose one which can be used either to produce plutonium as at Hanford or tritium, an H-bomb material which we shall describe in the next chapter. When completed it will be the world's most expensive single plant costing approximately $1.4 billion. This staggering total assumes significance only by comparison. It represents a larger capital outlay than the total for all the Bethlehem Steel Corporation installations, the latter being the third largest plant complex in the United States. Taken together with the Paducah plant the Savannah plant is roughly equal in value to that of the land, factories, and equipment of the General Motors Corporation.

Unlike the General Motors Corporation which each year turns out such a vast flood of consumer goods the new site on the Savannah River will turn out a mere trickle of the world's most expensive stuff—tritium. This is a form of hydrogen gas and, as we shall see later, is produced by irradiating lithium metal inside a nuclear reactor. The latter is understood to be of advanced design perhaps modeled after the heavy water reactor built at Chalk River, Canada. Heavy water is superior to graphite as a pile-moderating material and should make it possible to design smaller-size plants than those built at Hanford. Like the Hanford units the Savannah reactors generate huge amounts of power in the form of heat which is then removed by a heat exchanger through which is pumped cooling water. Some indication of the magnitude of the Savannah operation is given by the fact that the water pumping station has a capacity of 700 million gallons per day or enough to supply most of the city of New York with its daily water requirement.

When the Congress made its third round of atomic expansion appropriations it approved almost exactly $3 billion for new plant construction. $346 million went into building more plutonium-production units at Hanford. An additional $459 million went to build another diffusion plant at Paducah, Kentucky, thus doubling the size of that installation. The Oak Ridge diffusion plant was also expanded to the tune of $464 million. The biggest chunk of the appropriation went into building another huge gaseous diffusion plant near Portsmouth, Ohio. Some 6,500 acres in southern Ohio were acquired for the plant which when completed in 1956 will cost over $1.2 billion. New steam plants are being built to supply the 1,800,000 kilowatts of electricity which the new plant will demand. About seven million tons of coal will be required annually to fire up the boilers of these electrical generating stations.

The remainder of the $3 billion appropriation which the Congress provided during the summer of 1952 was allocated to additional facilities at the Savannah site and to providing new plants for processing the uranium feed material.

Facts and figures about the postwar construction of atomic facilities are very impressive. They tend to eclipse the record which the nation established during the war in building the huge plants at Hanford and Oak Ridge but they cannot obscure the fact that these were the first plants of their kind ever to be built in the world. Nor can they match the speed with which these plants were erected. Consider the spectacular fact that nine years later we are still duplicating these plants and yet the construction time is almost twice the wartime record.

Before long the nation will have invested almost $10 billion in its atomic energy program and it will have five separate sites which contain more than $1 billion worth of capital installations. Averaged over a decade this means that the United States has converted its atomic energy program into a $1 billion annual venture. All of this program has been aimed at producing tons of U-235 and Pu-239 for use in atomic explosives and the continued operation of the atomic plants assures the nation of a very large stockpile of these fissionable materials. Fortunately, as we shall see in the discussion of atomic power, this stockpile is not like a vast quantity of T.N.T. which is useful only for war. Our atomic stockpile is convertible to peacetime use for generating atomic power.

The great emphasis on new plant construction tends to make the quiet research in atomic laboratories seem of little consequence. Superficially, this would appear to be true for one cannot see much that is very substantial in a modern scientific laboratory whereas it is easy to be impressed by huge plants. However, the scientists in the AEC laboratories play a large part in the very practical matter of building up a bigger stockpile of atomic bombs. A single development, such as the perfection of a new barrier to work in the diffusion plant, can save millions of dollars each year and result in a substantial boost in the output of U-235 from that plant. At the other end of the line, in using the U-235 in an A-bomb, scientists can be even more effective. If the scientists and technicians at Los Alamos can work out a new way to explode an A-bomb more efficiently, that is, get more "bang" for the same amount of U-235 then they have in effect expanded the atomic stockpile. The extensive weapons tests which have been conducted at the Eniwetok Proving Grounds and in Nevada have evolved more efficient atomic bombs which in turn have stretched the stockpile of fissionable material. There is another factor which pertains to "breeding" of bomb material which I shall discuss subsequently; this may contribute significantly to the stockpile.

All in all, the combination of the increased weapon efficiency and the increased production of U-235 and Pu-239 adds up to a very substantial increase in our stockpile of atomic bombs. No reader would want me to spell out quantitatively how large the A-bomb stockpile is. Nor would I think of revealing such a figure even though the late Senator McMahon stated that a foreign power could estimate it accurately within 15 per cent. However, to orient the reader I can indicate that the stockpile must be numbered in the thousands of A-bombs. Moreover, when our enormous and far-flung grid of atomic facilities is completed and in full operation the goal of a 10,000-A-bomb stockpile should be in sight.

Aside from research and development on atomic weapons the Atomic Energy Commission has sponsored a very extensive program to promote basic research in the physical and life sciences. The Division of Biology and Medicine together with the Research Division of the AEC support major research programs in centers such as the Argonne National Laboratory near Chicago, the Brookhaven National Laboratory on Long Island, the Radiation Laboratory on the campus of the University of California, and the Oak Ridge National Laboratory. These four laboratories bear the brunt of the government's atomic research program.

There are in addition research centers at the University of Rochester, at Ames Laboratory, Ames, Iowa, at the University of California, Los Angeles, at Mound Laboratory, Miamisburg, Ohio. A special atomic power laboratory operated by the General Electric Company is located at Schenectady and is known as the Knolls Atomic Power Laboratory. All together these laboratories form the core of the AEC's research work but it is by no means all that the atomic agency does in research. It contracts with about one hundred universities, colleges, and research institutes to do "outside" research and development on problems of interest to the Commission. Dollarwise the total research bill of the AEC totals somewhat more than $70 million. This figure does not include money appropriated for the Reactor Division, the latter running well over $100 million if one includes the costs of new facilities being built.

There is little doubt that the atomic agency is research-minded as compared with other government agencies. It knows full well its whole program is delicately balanced upon the knife edge of future scientific developments. A single discovery today may become a million-dollar budget item next year. A single development in chemistry may make an existing chemical process obsolete and save the Commission millions of dollars. Knowing this some officials of the new agency have tried hard to get Congress to be more research-minded. However, many Congressmen have a distinct lack of enthusiasm for research. It is a paradox that they will appropriate a billion dollars for a new production facility but balk at a one-million-dollar budget item for research and development. This is, in part, understandable for production facilities of steel, brick, and concrete can be seen and the costs checked to see if there was waste or mismanagement. The average Congressman can see very little in ethereal research and has a deep-rooted suspicion that it is a bureaucratic boondoggle to waste the taxpayers' money. Furthermore the end results of research are hard to pin down and very difficult to explain to the taxpayer.

I find myself in an awkward position to pick out from the AEC research and development record a "case history" which will be dramatic and easily appreciated by the reader. What is dramatic to a scientist may be insipid to a lay reader whose experience lies far from the field of science. However, I believe that one event in the postwar atomic developments stands out above all others and I hope that I can communicate some of the significance of it.

The reader has undoubtedly heard of machines called cyclotrons but he may be pardoned if he does not know precisely what they are or how they work. They are essentially huge magnetic-electrical machines for whirling atoms around in circles inside an evacuated chamber until the atoms attain very high energy. Each time the atom makes one complete trip around the circuit it picks up a package of energy and after making many, many trips it may emerge with many million volts of energy. This is much like a boy on a merry-go-round who sticks out his hand once each trip around and grabs a hundred-dollar bill from a bystander (a wholly fictitious example!) until after many, many trips he becomes a millionaire. If everything went on as usual the boy could keep grabbing money and eventually become a billionaire but here our analogy breaks down for in the case of the cyclotron we have to deal with Mr. Einstein. The atoms whirling around at higher and higher speeds obey one of Mr. Einstein's rules that mass must increase with speed. So in being whirled around in a circle the atoms become heavier and consequently fail to arrive at the proper point in each circuit to gain energy. It is as though in the merry-go-round our boy stuck out his hand at the wrong time and missed grabbing the money. Before the war it seemed that there was nothing one could do about this problem and it looked like cyclotrons would only reach a certain energy and could go no higher. In fact, one physicist wrote a paper proving that the limit in energy was about 40 million volts.

Then immediately after the war ended an American physicist Dr. E. M. McMillan and, independently, a Russian scientist Dr. V. Veksler popped up with an idea to get around this impasse. We need not discuss the theory; it is sufficient that a new idea made it possible to design a supercyclotron one type of which is now called a cosmotron. Scientists and engineers at the AEC's Brookhaven National Laboratory, located at the site of old Camp Upton, went to work on the design of a huge magnetic-electrical machine to boost particles up to 2 billion volts in energy. It is a huge doughnutlike magnet about 75 feet in diameter weighing 2,200 tons. A vacuum tube nestles inside the magnet like an inner tube inside a tire and it is in this vacuum that atoms fly around and around so fast that in one second they travel a distance equal to that of six trips around the earth's equator. They pick up energy each time around the circuit until they reach a maximum of 2 billion volts.

The cosmotron operated successfully in the spring of 1952 and all the scientists from the many universities in northeastern U.S.A. who collaborated in the work were highly elated. At last they had a machine which would produce artificial cosmic rays. This marks a milestone in nuclear science for with the machine it should soon be possible to really convert mass into energy or vice versa. In uranium fission, mass is converted into energy but one only taps about .1 per cent of the uranium's energy. What one does is to rearrange the 235 particles in a U-235 nucleus into two smaller atoms but the total number of particles is still 235, although the weight is less. The difference in weight appears as energy. One does not take one of these particles and convert it into energy. With the cosmotron it should be possible to achieve this real mass-energy conversion and artificially produce an atom. This does not mean that there will be an immediate practical result but the way will be paved for further exploration of the atom and perhaps eventually man will be armed to get more than .1 per cent of the atom's energy. Even as these words are written, scientists at the Brookhaven National Laboratory have announced that a new principle of operation should permit boosting particles up to 100 billion volts of energy.

If this event marked the high peak of success in the postwar research program then in contrast there is a single event which marked a rock-bottom low. It was the investigation touched off by the reported loss of some uranium from the Argonne National Laboratory near Chicago. Spearheaded by Iowa's redoubtable Senator Bourke Hickenlooper, the investigation took off on a futile hunt to find peanut-sized amounts of enriched uranium. This amounted to less than a drop in our uranium supply bucket but the Congressional search served to stop almost all work in several atomic sites while the chase was on. It may be remarked here that the AEC keeps account of its uranium inventory as carefully as our gold is watched over in Fort Knox.

Looking back on the atomic developments of the postwar period one can see that the threat of World War III cast the entire AEC work in a quite different light from what would have been if it could have concentrated on peacetime application of atomic energy. The main job of the Commission became one of building new plants to keep up with an ever-growing demand for fissionable material and at the same time to perfect new atomic weapons. This process became almost a tobogganlike operation for no sooner were plants completed to fulfill the military demand than new atomic weapons were developed which created a new military demand for more bomb material.

5

DESTRUCTION UNLIMITED

Wʜᴇɴ President Truman first announced that a bomb equal to the explosive force of 20,000 tons of T.N.T. had been detonated over Japan one would have been justified in thinking that the ultimate weapon had been achieved. But as subsequent developments were to prove, this was only the beginning. Bigger and bigger atomic weapons were to be developed. Emphasis in the postwar bomb work focused on making atomic weapons which dwarfed the Nagasaki bomb and within the short span of seven years the H-bomb, the Gargantua of weapons, was born.

The tip-off on future developments in atomic weaponry is contained in a brief paragraph from Dr. Edward Teller's testimony before Congress on February 1, 1946. This noted bomb expert foretold the nature of coming events most prophetically in these words:

> The atomic bomb is in its earliest infancy and even a moderate amount of work may improve it considerably. Future bombs may become less expensive, may be easier to handle, and they may have a much greater destructive power. I am convinced that it will not be very difficult to construct atomic bombs which will dwarf the Hiroshima bomb in the same way that that bomb has dwarfed high explosives.

Obviously, Dr. Teller was thinking of the H-bomb when he made the last remark and five years later he spearheaded the theoretical work which paved the way for that weapon.

Even before the Atomic Energy Commission had been established, the Navy Department urged that a series of A-bombs be exploded to determine the effects of atomic weapons on ships. During the development of the A-bomb, and even in the postwar period that followed, information about the weapon was limited to a very few military personnel. One result of isolating the weapon from the men responsible for its employment was to give rise to wild speculation about the impact of the A-bomb upon the art of war. Pseudomilitary experts foresaw the quick obsolescence of the Navy. The admirals were not unmindful of the effect that such speculation would have upon the Congress and its willingness to support a strong postwar Navy, so they decided to face the issue squarely and conduct a huge experiment in which a fleet of ships would be exposed to the violence of an atomic explosion. Early in 1946 a series of bomb tests were scheduled to be held in the summer at a tiny atoll in the vastness of the Pacific Ocean. The site was Bikini—a slender necklace of scimitar-shaped islands over 2,000 miles southwest of Hawaii.

At this time I was still in Chicago working at the Argonne National Laboratory trying to make up my mind whether to stick in the pure field of science or to go astray from it. I decided that a junket to the South Pacific might help me make up my mind so before anyone in the laboratory had time to object I had organized a group of thirty scientists to participate in the Bikini tests. We armed ourselves with scores of Geiger counters and other radiation measurement devices which we had made ourselves for we were suspicious of the instruments which the Army said it would provide for the tests. Our suspicions were later shown to be well founded. Our instruments worked; those provided by the Army worked erratically.

The Army, Navy, and the Air Corps had teamed up as Joint Task Force One to conduct a series of three tests. Test Able was to be an air burst, Test Baker an underwater explosion near the lagoon surface, and Test Charlie a deep underwater burst. The latter never came off. For Test Able almost one hundred ships were anchored close together. The brightly painted *Nevada,* a U.S. battleship, swung at anchor in the center of the target fleet and a few ship lengths away the Japanese battlewagon *Nagato* rolled slightly in the choppy waters of the lagoon. Farther away was the sleek *Prinz Eugen,* the German pocket battleship, and at varying distances were transports, submarines, landing ships, destroyers, and even an aircraft carrier. All the ships were arrayed closer together than they would have been in normal anchorage so that the test was not rigged, as some claimed, to yield results favorable to the Navy. Test Able went off as slated except that the bomb dropped from a B-29 at an altitude of 30,000 feet missed its mark considerably, falling so far from its intended mark above the *Nevada* that much of the measuring equipment failed to function properly.

I recall that many newsmen upon surveying the damage to the target fleet were not much impressed with the power of the A-bomb. Some went so far as to describe it as a "giant firecracker."

What they failed to realize is that a ship is a rugged structure, more strongly built than a modern building and quite unlike a building it can roll with the punch absorbing much impact by recoiling in the water. Conditioned by the catastrophic structural damage in Hiroshima and Nagasaki reporters were distinctly disappointed in the results of the first atomic explosion at Bikini. They looked forward anxiously to the results of Test Baker for never before had an A-bomb been exploded underwater.

Weird stories were published or were spread by word of mouth about what would happen when the A-bomb was detonated below the calm surface of the Bikini lagoon. Some predicted that an enormous tidal wave would be produced and might even thunder across the Pacific to inundate Hawaii. Others made dark predictions about mysterious things which would happen to the ocean when it was excited by the angry lash of the atom. The prophets of doom were muttering in their beards and uttering their strange and dire incantations. Man was nudging nature's secrets too intimately; surely he would be catastrophically punished for his brashness. Such were the prophecies.

What was foretold did not come to pass. The bomb was exploded without creating a tidal wave. In fact, the wave which rolled toward the shores of Bikini, some three miles away, was no more than six feet high and it did not inundate the flyspeck island. Nor did the sea water ignite and consume the world in an all embracing flame of destruction. But something did happen which paid the prophets big dividends. Radioactivity became their constant obsession. The myth of radioactivity had been born at Hiroshima with the explosion of the A-bomb there but it had almost died out when the city was promptly inhabited and found to be habitable. The gossamer bomb cloud which had mushroomed over Hiroshima had carried with it all the sting of any persistent danger from radioactive atoms. These had been harmlessly dispersed in the stratosphere where they were carried around the world to be detected by delicate measuring instruments. Dispersed in the enormous reaches of the upper atmosphere the invisible radioactive particles ceased to be of any hazard to mankind. However, when the A-bomb was exploded well below the surface of the Bikini lagoon all this enormous aggregate of radioactive material released by the bomb did not vanish in the heavens. Quite the contrary, most of it was trapped in the lagoon or was only hurled briefly into the sky thereupon falling down upon the target fleet, drenching its decks with a heavy contamination of radioactivity.

I recall very vividly what happened at Bikini after Test Baker. The little gunboat on which I was technically in charge nosed into the lagoon and within two hours edged into the target fleet. Our Geiger counters chattered and I made a careful check to see that all our instruments were operating properly. We had already consigned the Army instruments to an electronic limbo. On our own instrument dials the needles edged across the scales indicating that the radioactivity in the area was going up. Things were getting hotter. I discovered that the ship's screws were churning radioactive water upward and making things hotter so I asked the skipper to back off and coast into the target fleet. This maneuver worked and soon we were well in toward the center close to the *Prinz Eugen*. Sailors who by this time had become intensely interested in our chattering instruments were peering over my shoulder, fascinated by the dial needle which was knocking against its upper limit. I explained rather nonchalantly that we were at the "tolerance limit" and would go no further. Noticing a Navy veteran gulp and register alarm I hastily explained that we were operating under laboratory rules, and no one would be permitted to absorb any more radiation than if he were back in the United States working in one of the atomic plants. To reassure them I added that I had received this tolerance amount of radiation more than once and it had never hurt me. Actually, it was the ambiguity of the word "tolerance" which caused so much confusion in the public mind about this hazard. We treated everyone at Bikini as though they would be duplicating their Bikini experience every day of their life. Since it was a one-shot affair we could have allowed them one hundred times as much exposure to radioactivity as we did. And if it had been a wartime operation we could have upped this limit a thousand fold.

At Bikini there were observers who had previously had no acquaintance with radioactivity. To them the click-click of a Geiger counter was akin to a rattlesnake's warning. They failed to appreciate that even the most fearful rattle of a Geiger instrument may be absolutely no cause for alarm. These instruments are so sensitive that they record the passage of a single radioactive ray whereas it takes millions of them passing through the counter to show that one is in mortal danger. A few awe-struck onlookers at Bikini became the disciples of a new cult. Upon returning to the United States they stomped the country preaching the gospel that radioactivity would be man's downfall. They found a ready audience for as eyewitnesses to the bomb tests they became automatically enrolled as the chief prophets. Their words carried a ring of authenticity mostly because they spoke of strange things and they had all the mystic appeal of the unknown. Furthermore, the prophets had the ability to make headlines. Just imagine a newsman passing up a choice morsel such as the prediction, "Exploding 100 A-bombs anywhere in the world will make life on earth impossible." Once attracted by the magnetic appeal of page

1 some of the prophets became more and more hysterical, fearful lest their press notices appear on the financial page.

In the years since Bikini the prophets of doom have managed to run out of wind but none the less they managed to instill fear of radioactivity into the populace far beyond the normal respect which this hazard should command. The result has been to induce apathy and despair in certain areas of civil defense. At the local level civil defense planning suffered severely as authorities struggled to cope with problems so enormous that solutions were impossible. People developed a pathological fear that some dark night a bomb would be exploded in a nearby river, lake, or reservoir sending a Bikini-like mist of radioactivity to snuff out silently a whole city while it slept. The Mississippi flowing around St. Louis and Lake Michigan bordering Chicago are quite unlike the Bikini lagoon.

Trying to dispel rumors or to deflate sensationalism is not an easy assignment. People are always more attracted to the bold headlines than they are to quiet refutations. The Navy found this out when five years after Bikini it towed a Bikini test ship out into the Pacific and sank it explaining this action quite carefully in a public announcement. But few bothered to note the complete wording of the announcement; they jumped to the conclusion that even after five years some naval vessels were still too hot for the Navy to handle. This was not the case. The Navy was merely taking pains to see that the mildly radioactive ship did not get dismantled in the regular way. Had this happened the steel might have been remelted and incorporated into instruments or equipment which would have interfered with radioactive measurements in research laboratories. The test ship was not a death trap; it was merely a possible inconvenience to the scientist.

It is my impression that the Navy profited from its Bikini adventure. It gave firsthand knowledge about atomic weapons to thousands of naval personnel and it served as a powerful stimulus for naval officers to start thinking about atomic weapons. It probably overindoctrinated the Navy in radioactivity, giving it a first-class "hot foot" as it were, but even this proved useful as the Navy thereafter established a laboratory to deal with problems created by the radioactive hazard. It is true that much of the Bikini test was in a sense a gigantic show and in some ways a clever publicity stunt. The scientific results of the test were almost invisible despite much ado about what science would learn from them. Both the bombs used in the tests were of the Nagasaki type. These were unimproved plutonium bombs equivalent to 20,000 tons of T.N.T.—more technically known as 20 kt bombs. Scientists at Los Alamos had wanted to try out an improved design but the Navy remained adamant on using the same kind as had blasted Nagasaki.

After these bomb tests the Atomic Energy Commission was established and during 1947 new designs of atomic weapons were evolved. This work centered at the Los Alamos where during the war the brilliant J. Robert Oppenheimer had held together a near critical mass of top-flight physicists—this being an accomplishment almost as neat as making the A-bomb, itself. When he left Los Alamos to return to university life and thereafter to head up the Institute for Advanced Studies at Princeton, Dr. Oppenheimer led a general exodus from the weapons laboratory. This constituted a very serious blow to weapon development. It is true that scientists also left the other laboratories of the Manhattan Project but in many respects their loss was not so serious because the tough problems they worked on in wartime had been solved. Oak Ridge and Hanford were realities. No galaxy of scientists was required to keep them in full operation.

With atomic weapons, however, the problem was quite different. As Dr. Teller pointed out, the science was still in its infancy.

Very few things of science are born in any state of perfection. In the field of internal combustion engines it required half a century to evolve from the puny sputtering engines of the early 1900's to the mass-produced precision motors of today. There was no reason to believe that atomic weapons would prove any exception to the rule. As regards the 1945-model A-bombs, the Atomic Energy Commission officially described them as "literally laboratory products, experimental devices not only designed but also largely fabricated and assembled by the distinguished scientists who conceived them." Thus there was room for considerable improvement in atomic weapons.

In the first two years following the end of the war the development of new weapons marked time. When the AEC took stock of the weapons situation in 1947 it found itself with the major problem of somehow making up for the loss of the brilliant scientists who had worked there up to 1945. The country was at peace, the best scientists were back at their regular tasks working away at fundamental research, and they had little inclination to disappear once again behind the barbed wire of Los Alamos where their work would be ultra-secret and much less interesting than the things they would do if left to their own devices. This tough problem was not completely solved but progress was made when it was decided that scientists at Los Alamos could spend a portion of their time working on their own research and that this work could be freely published. Partial solution was also provided by enlisting "summer scientists," that is, by inviting top scientists to spend their summers at Los Alamos.

By 1948 new designs for A-bombs were completed and the weapons were ready for testing. Unlike many scientific developments which can be tested on a small scale and then scaled up, A-bombs must be tested full scale or not at all. Therefore it was imperative that A-bombs be exploded. The question which arose then was finding the proper place to detonate them. Eniwetok Atoll was chosen in 1947 as the test site or more properly—the Atomic Proving Grounds. Located about 200 miles due west of Bikini the atoll is a typical island group with typically phonetic names such as Engebi, Biijiri-to, Igurin, and Bogallua. Islands such as Engebi were selected as separate test sites and throngs of construction workers were imported to pour the concrete and erect the iron towers for detonating and observing the bomb explosion. Work was rushed through to completion for the AEC was anxious to try out its new weapon designs and the Armed Forces were just as anxious to see what effects these bombs would have on tanks, aircraft, and a hundred odd pieces of military equipment. All three branches of the Military Establishment co-operated with the civilians of the AEC in a joint program called OPERATION SANDSTONE.

The spring of 1948 saw three improved type A-bombs tested in the pre-dawn darkness of the South Pacific. All three weapons equaled or exceeded the hopes of their designers. The only statement made by the Atomic Energy Commission was: "Operation Sandstone confirms the fact that the position of the United States in the field of atomic weapons has been substantially improved." Senator Edwin C. Johnson let the cat out of the bag as to how much "substantially" meant when he revealed: "Now our scientists already have created a bomb that has six times the effectiveness of the bomb that was dropped at Nagasaki." This (allowing for the Senator's loose language in failing to distinguish between "effectiveness" and power) would put the *explosive* power of the improved A-bomb at 120,000 tons of T.N.T. or in bomb language at 120 kt.

Development of the big A-bomb should have come as no surprise to anyone who had noted a speech given in December, 1946, by John J. McCloy, the assistant Secretary of War: "We talk today of the bomb in terms of the equivalent of 20,000 tons of T.N.T. From firsthand information given me by scientists whose prophecies were uncannily accurate during the course of the war, there can be little doubt that within the next ten years, to be conservative, bombs of the power equivalent to 100,000 to 250,000 tons of T.N.T. can be made." Mr. McCloy was conservative in his estimate of the time which would be required for the bomb development.

OPERATION SANDSTONE provided the first really scientific tests of atomic weapons. The first A-bomb which was exploded on July 16, 1945, at Alamogordo was a "quick and dirty" test which showed that an A-bomb would work but it revealed very little of the complicated chain of events which takes place within the bomb core in time intervals of less than one-ten-millionth of one second. A-bombs Nos. 2 and 3 were military demonstrations over Japan and they did not yield any intimate knowledge of what makes an A-bomb tick. Bombs Nos. 4 and 5 were set off at Bikini and gave only fragmentary data and these pertained to old-type weapons. However, bombs 6, 7, and 8 exploded on the tiny islands of the Eniwetok Atoll were truly scientific tests. The islands were spotted at fixed intervals from the bomb tower with clusters of every imaginable type of instrument. Miles of coaxial cable crisscrossed the concrete strips and rested in the sandy surface of the island. When the bombs were detonated the scientists for the first time obtained an "X-ray picture" of what happened inside the chain-reacting bomb prior to the time it blew itself apart. Data obtained from these tests formed the basis for understanding precisely how an A-bomb works. They permitted bomb experts to design even more powerful and more efficient weapons. This test series did not provide any experimental data on the H-bomb directly although it did indirectly contribute to the development since, as will be seen later, the attainment of a big A-bomb is essential to making an H-bomb.

A word or two must be said here about bomb efficiency. Any details are held ultra-secret by the Atomic Energy Commission and I would not reveal them if I could but in broad outline the problem of weapon efficiency may be discussed. Suppose that we assume that the bomb core of the 1945 model weapon was a sphere of U-235 or plutonium about the size of a baseball. This, as we know, yielded an explosion equal to 20,000 tons of T.N.T., the latter all being considered to be a single pile of explosives detonated simultaneously. Now not all of the U-235 or bomb material was fissioned or burned up in the chain reaction; in other words the efficiency was not 100 per cent. Efficiency is simply the percentage of the bomb material which is used up in the explosion. If by improving the bomb design the efficiency of the Nagasaki weapon could be doubled then the explosion would be twice as great. Instead of a 20,000 ton T.N.T. explosion (or a 20 kt bomb) we would have a 40 kt bomb. So with the same baseball-size charge of fissionable material one gets twice the explosive power from the bomb. This means that in effect you are making the uranium dollar stretch twice as far. Or, in other words, the bomb stockpile is doubled. Thus by improving weapon design one neatly expands the bomb stockpile just as though one had doubled the output of the Hanford works or the Oak Ridge plants.

Of course, there is a limit to the extent to which efficiency can be increased. You can't exceed 100 per cent and as a general rule in nature very few devices ever approach 100 per cent efficiency. Even with the advantage of decades of intensive development most electric generating plants are usually only 30 per cent efficient in their use of coal. The most modern is only 38 per cent efficient. So if you want to make bigger atomic bombs you are ultimately limited by the amount of fissionable material in the weapon. This is easy to remedy for one can simply add more U-235 or plutonium to the bomb core. Only in doing so you have to use some tricks for the bomb has to be kept below critical size before it is exploded. These tricks constitute our bomb secrets or what we hope are secrets. That the big A-bombs use more bomb material is substantiated by Gordon Dean, chairman of the AEC, in testifying on the 1953 budget request. He stated: "Certainly, the new designs of weapons are such that you would use a lot of material."

Since bigger A-bombs do consume more valuable U-235 or plutonium it is reasonable to ask whether or not the same amount of material invested in two smaller bombs might not be a better way to use the material. Strictly on the basis of explosive power we can make the following argument. The area subject to severe blast damage from a 20 kt bomb is 4.6 square miles; this defines a circle with a radius of slightly less than 1¼ miles. The area hit by a 40 kt bomb is not twice as large, as at first might be thought, but is 7 square miles, that is a circular area with radius of 1½ miles. Thus doubling the power of the bomb does not double the damage area but increases by slightly more than 50 per cent. If instead of purely geometrical areas we consider an actual target we may find the disparity even more discordant for not all targets are perfectly circular; some are elongated and on them a bigger bomb wastes much of its explosive power.

To this so-called area argument may be added another. That is the fact that with smaller A-bombs one can still maintain a semblance of humanity in bombing for these still have the element of selectivity. Even though the smaller bomb knocks out several square miles one can maintain that the industrial section of a city is the target whereas with a big bomb there is no selectivity. You saturate the target in an all-engulfing wave of destruction without distinguishing between military targets and nonmilitary areas. This, of course, raises the moral issue with respect to strategic bombing. Smaller A-bombs which can be limited to purely military targets or to military sections of a target can be exempt from the moral argument but the big city-buster models cannot.

The Air Force has been the ardent champion of bigger and bigger A-bombs. Its principal arguments are these. First, delivery of A-bombs under wartime conditions may be extremely difficult and bomber penetration through enemy defenses may be subject to such high attrition that we must gamble on getting a small number of big A-bombs to their targets rather than a larger number of smaller weapons. Second, the cost of building and maintaining a strategic striking force of modern bombers is fearfully expensive. The bomber is not only more important than the bomb—it is actually more costly in terms of dollars and cents. Emphasis should therefore concentrate on maintaining a smaller force of high-speed bombers equipped to deliver big A-bombs. Finally, under battle conditions the accurate delivery of bombs cannot be guaranteed. It is therefore better to have a weapon which has a larger striking radius so as to compensate for any bombing error.

One must add to these reasons still another factor which focused attention on making bigger and still bigger A-bombs. It is simply the American mania for making things bigger on the basis that they are also better. Indeed, some bomb experts at Los Alamos became so engrossed with making bigger A-bombs that they failed to inquire very carefully into other type developments —namely into making smaller A-bombs; this is a subject we shall treat in a later chapter. I mention the fact here because preoccupation with big strategic A-bombs definitely hindered work on smaller A-bombs.

A big push in the direction of bigger bombs was given by the first series of tests at the Eniwetok Proving Grounds in 1948. Three years later another series of four atomic bomb explosions was detonated and later described officially as "several times more powerful than the Hiroshima and Nagasaki weapons." These tests were more carefully planned than the first series and were much more comprehensive. A Joint Task Force directed by Lieutenant General Quesada comprised 9,000 participating personnel. Known as OPERATION GREENHOUSE the second test program included elaborate instrumentation to assess the effects of the improved bombs on structures such as concrete buildings, on military vehicles such as tanks and aircraft, and on assorted military gear including Geiger counters, clothing, and ordnance equipment. Biologists and medical men also made the long trek across the Pacific to the proving grounds to study the effects of the bomb on animals.

Contrary to published accounts none of the four bombs tested were dropped from aircraft. All were exploded atop tall steel towers anchored in reinforced concrete bases and it may be assumed that these towers like the one at Alamogordo vanished with the bomb explosion leaving only iron stubs jutting from the buried concrete. The aircraft which were used in these tests were for purposes of observation of the detonation itself as well as for guinea pig use to observe the direct blast effect on the planes. Over one hundred planes were employed ranging from light liaison aircraft up to the heavy B-47s and B-50s.

Since there are only a limited number of suitable islands comprising the Eniwetok group some had to be used for more than one shot. Brigadier General James Cooney described the reoccupation of one island after an atomic test as follows: "Full time work started 1,000 yards from the detonation point on the day of the explosion and within 72 hours required to build barracks, the workers occupied their quarters." This flat statement of fact by an Army officer experienced in radiation protection should serve to dispel fear that bombed cities would be uninhabitable for any considerable period of time.

The Greenhouse tests which took place in April and May of 1951 also included some novel and complex experiments on thermonuclear reactions or in more popular language—on the H-bomb. However, this is getting us ahead of our story and we must backtrack to November 1, 1949. The scene is a television studio in New York City. A program is in progress in which Senator Edwin C. Johnson of Colorado is debating with some scientists the question: "Is there too much secrecy in our atomic program?" Suddenly the Senator amazed his colleagues: "Here's the thing that is top secret," he said. "Our scientists from the time that the bombs were detonated at Hiroshima and Nagasaki have been trying to make what is known as a superbomb." Referring to the six times more powerful bomb developed at Eniwetok the Senator continued: "They want one that has a thousand times the effect of that terrible bomb—and that's the secret, the big secret that scientists in America are so anxious to divulge to the whole scientific world."

Later Senator Johnson stoutly denied that he had violated security, maintaining that three years before John J. McCloy, whom we have already quoted, stated: "If we can move to the other end of the periodic table and use hydrogen in the generation of energy, we would have a bomb somewhere around 1,000 times as powerful as the Nagasaki bomb." One might argue, however, that McCloy's statement was only an estimate of a possibility; it contained no description of American work in progress on such a weapon. Officials within the Atomic Energy Commission were flabbergasted by the public disclosure. Previously, the very mention of the weapon was confined to triple-locked rooms and referred to ambiguously as "super."

After the initial break on the H-bomb, secrecy again closed in on the work. Further developments might have been completely screened from public view had it not been for the expert reporting of Alfred Friendly (Washington *Post*) and the Alsop brothers. On January 2, 1950, Joseph and Stewart Alsop wrote in their syndicated column about secret decisions on the H-bomb: "Thus dustily and obscurely, the issues of life and death are settled nowadays—dingy committee rooms are the scenes of the debate; harassed officials are the disputants; all the proceedings are highly classified; yet the whole future hangs, perhaps, upon the outcome." Arguing that the debate must be brought out into the open they concluded that: "This must be done, since deeper issues are involved which have been far too long concealed from the country."

On January 31, 1950, President Truman made the announcement of a go-ahead on the H-bomb project. His statement is as follows: "It is part of my responsibility as Commander in Chief of the armed forces to see to it that our country is able to defend itself against any possible aggressor. Accordingly, I have directed the Atomic Energy Commission to continue its work on all forms of atomic weapons, including the so-called hydrogen or super-bomb."

A few days later the noted Dr. Oppenheimer, speaking with

Mrs. Roosevelt on a TV program, warned that: "It is a grave danger for us that these decisions are being made on the basis of facts held secret. This is not because those who contributed to the decisions or make them are lacking in wisdom, it is because wisdom itself cannot flourish and even the truth cannot be established, without the give and take of debate and criticism. The facts, the relevant facts, are of little use to an enemy, yet they are fundamental to an understanding of the issues of policy."

Almost as if in answer to Dr. Oppenheimer's plea for public discussion of the H-bomb issue, a group of scientists independently began a series of articles in the *Scientific American* magazine. Leading off was an article by Louis N. Ridenour, dean of the Graduate College at the University of Illinois. Significantly, this scientist had not worked on the A-bomb project. His publication in March, 1950, must have served to alert and alarm certain officials within the Atomic Energy Commission for fireworks broke out on the following issue of the series. If a pun be allowed, the issue became very hot, for 3,000 copies of the April issue were ordered burned by the AEC. At the time I was busy writing what was to be the third in the series and I had received a mimeographed copy of the second article written by the world-famous Dr. Hans A. Bethe, professor of physics at Cornell University. When I received an urgent notice to return Dr. Bethe's article my curiosity was aroused and I perused the mimeographed pages to see what had occasioned so much concern. It was an excellently written story and I found nothing to get excited about from a security viewpoint so making mental notes as to possible disputed passages I mailed the article back to the publisher. Then when the magazine was finally published I compared my mental notes with the censored version of the article. There was only a trivial discrepancy. Apparently, the entire matter was meant to be palpable proof that the AEC was carefully guarding its H-bomb secrets. For as our A-bomb monopoly vanished desperate souls in the nation's capitol sought to retrieve a sense of security by establishing an H-bomb monopoly.

Dr. Bethe may be regarded as the father of the H-bomb for it was his pioneer work on studying the source of our sun's energy that gave the world basic knowledge about thermonuclear reactions. This word—thermonuclear—means heat-produced nuclear reaction. In trying to puzzle through the mystery of the sun's constant liberation of energy Dr. Bethe soon arrived at the conclusion that the amounts of energy involved were so vast that only nuclear reactions could account for the heat produced. He knew that at the center of the sun a very high temperature existed, probably over 20 million degrees centigrade and he also knew that deep within the sun even gaseous hydrogen was compressed to the point where it weighed seven times as much as lead. His attention focused on hydrogen for two reasons. First, there is such a large proportion of this element in our sun. Second, hydrogen is the lightest element known and the laws of physics require that for any given temperature the hydrogen atoms should have the greatest speed. The latter point is very important since nuclear reactions work best at high speed and this is the reason why cyclotrons are used to study many such reactions; they whirl hydrogen atoms around to speeds which cannot be attained in our sun.

Knowing that our sun has lots of hydrogen in it and that these atoms bombard one another fiercely, the Cornell University physicist was confronted with the real puzzler of finding some chain of events, that is, a series of nuclear reactions, which would release energy at a rate that would account for the sun's heat. He hit upon what is now known as the Carbon cycle or the Bethe cycle. It may be described qualitatively as a long-drawn-out process, taking well over a million years for each cycle, in which four hydrogen atoms fuse together to form a single atom of helium. Carbon atoms enter into the business merely as sort of a holding company. First, a hydrogen atom bumps into a carbon atom and gets captured by it; this is a very rare phenomenon, for it takes about a million years for a carbon atom and a hydrogen atom to get together and become welded together. It takes roughly 200,000 years for the next event to happen—that is the addition of a second hydrogen atom to this converted carbon atom. Then, in a much longer time, another H-atom fuses into this twice-converted atom and finally the fourth H-atom sticks in this nucleus and an atom of helium is born. We call the process hydrogen fusion.

At first, it may seem very strange to the layman that the fusion or welding together of hydrogen atoms to form a single heavier atom should release energy for in the case of uranium we saw that it was the fission or splitting of a heavy atom into two parts which released energy. The ground rules that nature has laid down for the construction of atoms are such that if you split an atom of helium into hydrogen atoms you do not release energy. In fact it takes considerable energy to do this trick—the same amount that you get back if you can persuade the H-atoms to combine again.

When Dr. Bethe first announced his discovery way back during the depression days no one was very much excited about an H-bomb although physicists and astrophysicists were very much excited about the successful explanation of the sun's enormous energy. After all, anything that takes well over a million years to happen is a mighty slow explosion. Anyway, man had no means at his disposal to duplicate the intense temperatures and pressures generated deep within the center of our sun. But the perversity of nature has shown two ways around these obstacles. Man has learned to duplicate at least for a millionth of a second the fiery heat of the sun through his perfection of the atomic bomb. Man has also discovered a way to compress the multimillion year explosion time in the sun to a millionth of a second on earth. He has found that no H-bomb would be possible using ordinary hydrogen such as is found in the sun or in natural gas wells. However, there are two other kinds of hydrogen—we call them hydrogen isotopes—which will work in an H-bomb.

We shall not dip very deeply into H-bomb technology except to point out the origin of these hydrogen isotopes. One is heavy hydrogen—or deuterium if the reader prefers the scientific name—and the other is extra-heavy hydrogen or tritium. Heavy hydrogen may be produced without too great difficulty by recovering it from water. There is a slight fraction of the hydrogen in water which is heavy hydrogen and it can be separated out in ton lots. However, heavy hydrogen alone does not work in an H-bomb. You need tritium to go along with it. Tritium cannot be won from nature in the same way as heavy hydrogen because it it not there to begin with; you have to manufacture it by a process very similar to that used in making plutonium. In fact, you can use the same plants as were used in making plutonium and by substituting the light element lithium instead of uranium the tritium can be produced.

Shortly after the President's announcement of a go-ahead on the H-project the Congress appropriated funds for the Savannah River site which was discussed earlier. Although described in the newspapers as an H-plant it is a dual-purpose installation capable of producing either plutonium or tritium. It consists of a reactor farm, that is, a number of reactor units similar to those built at Hanford but of more modern design—smaller and more economical to operate. Prior to the start-up of the Savannah River plants enough tritium was produced at the Hanford works to permit the exploratory work which was conducted on the lonely Eniwetok Atoll in the spring of 1951. The experiments on thermonuclear reactions carried out in OPERATION GREENHOUSE were of the ultra-small-scale type but they paved the way for larger-scale tests a year and a half later. Continued production at the Hanford plants supplied enough tritium to permit the spectacular initial H-test held in the fall of 1952.

By way of introduction to the mechanism of the H-bomb let us compare the energy released in hydrogen fusion with that set free in uranium fission. When a heavy hydrogen and a tritium atom fuse together you get only about one-twelfth the energy which is released from the splitting of a single uranium atom. In practice not all uranium atoms can be fissioned in an A-bomb and one would expect even fewer hydrogen atoms to fuse together in an H-bomb. As a rough guess one can estimate that it takes about five or ten pounds of liquid heavy hydrogen to produce an explosion equal to one nominal A-bomb, i.e., a 20 kt model. Conceivably it might take much more, depending upon how clever the designers were in detonating the bomb.

Unlike an A-bomb which is limited in the amount of uranium which can be used because of critical size, the H-bomb is an open-ended weapon. That is, you can pour as much hydrogen into it as you desire provided you have the hydrogen and can perfect a bomb mechanism which will keep the whole bomb together long enough for the explosion to fuse a significant fraction of the H-atoms together before the heat blows the weapon apart. Very often in the press a thousand-fold more powerful H-bomb has been mentioned. Such a bomb, even if detonated with high efficiency, would require for the bomb fuel 1,000 times the five to ten pounds of hydrogen needed for a Nagasaki bomb. This means that for just the fuel alone one would have to have more than two tons of deuterium-tritium mixture. Obviously, the auxiliary apparatus required to detonate such a bomb would be massive for the fuel alone would fill a sphere five feet in diameter. The problem of making such a big bomb is a practical one, namely, of finding some way to wrap the triggering A-bomb around the hydrogen core and still have the whole bomb detonate properly.

Once we consider a bomb that is in the megaton (i.e., million tons of T.N.T) size range it is not too important whether the bomb is 1, 2, 10, or 20 megatons. Already the damage area from the 1 megaton bomb is so great that it effectively blankets almost any target of military significance. For example, a 1-megaton H-bomb deals heavy devastation to 60 square miles of area and moderate damage to 110 square miles. Such a bomb would strike severely over the built up sections of metropolitan cities like St. Louis, Washington, or Boston and considerable damage would extend well into the suburbs. The core of all but a half-dozen American cities is less than 100 square miles in extent. Even beyond the city limits of the metropolitan areas damage would be inflicted on exposed people by the tremendous solarlike flash of heat from the H-bomb. The 1-megaton bomb would send forth light and heat in such huge quantities that it would sear everything within 70 square miles and skin burns would be produced in a circular area 13 miles in diameter. Penetrating radiation would also be emitted but, if it is any consolation, this would be confined to a relatively small area. The latter effect would be reduced by the requirement that the H-bomb be detonated high in the air in order to spread out its destruction over the widest possible distance.

This, then, is the H-bomb. What we have described is not the ultimate in H-weapons but *only* a 1-megaton bomb. Still larger and more destructive H-bombs are possible. The actual size of the superbomb is not the theoretical limit but rather the one imposed by the ingenuity of the bomb designers, by the ability of aircraft to carry the huge weapon, and by the military requirement. With respect to the last mentioned point Dr. Robert F. Bacher, first scientist member of the Atomic Energy Commission, had some extremely pertinent remarks in a speech he gave after resigning from the AEC. Addressing himself to the question: "How important is the hydrogen bomb to national security?" Dr. Bacher stated: "While it is a terrible weapon its military effectiveness seems to have been grossly overrated in the mind of the layman. . . . Quantities of hydrogen bombs will not contribute very much to the security of the United States." This sober admonition should be pondered carefully for the man who made it is not only a top-flight scientist but he served during the war as a leading bomb expert at Los Alamos and later, as a Commissioner of the AEC, he had access to top-secret atomic and military data to which few scientists are privy.

Possession of even a sizable stockpile of H-bombs will not greatly enhance the military status of the United States vis-à-vis Russia because we already have a sufficient stockpile of improved A-bombs to execute a strategic blitz of the Soviet homeland. When you have A-weapons each of which can knock out twenty-five-square-mile areas you do not gain very much when you substitute H-weapons each of which may have the ability to deal the same destruction to four times that area. There are a limited number of targets behind the Iron Curtain that will qualify as H-targets. On the other hand within the borders of the United States there are truly prime targets for a Soviet H-bomb. If the Soviet Union has a limited atomic stockpile then it will place great emphasis upon the H-bomb, and we may be sure that a U.S. hydrogen bomb monopoly will be a short-lived affair. With its huge concentrations of people, so well illustrated by the multitudes within line of sight of fifty television transmitters, the United States will awake someday to realize that the H-bomb actually weakens its position with respect to the U.S.S.R.

For the first time since this nation gained its independence, it is faced with the threat of an attack which may knock out its cities, their thousands of factories, and their millions of people. Yet the American people, by and large, have ducked this issue. They have preferred not to look at the face of danger. As a result the United States many years after Hiroshima is not prepared for an atomic attack.

I feel very strongly about the subject of atomic defense; so much so that it is only with the exercise of great self-control that I refrain from devoting all the remaining chapters to this topic. But this is not a book about atomic defense. I cannot, however, pass over the subject without mentioning that it is absolute nonsense to assume that "There is no defense against the A-bomb," as so many people have said. Or against the H-bomb, for that matter. There never was a weapon against which some defense was not possible. Of course, there is no magic defense against nuclear weapons. There is no "death ray" which can flick out into the skies and detonate an A-bomb as it nestles in the bomb bay of an enemy bomber. But, given the money, time, and resourcefulness, we may find a defense against the bomber.

Scientific developments which have taken place since 1950 show rather clearly that it should be possible to erect the substance of a continental defense capable of repelling or killing the majority of invading aircraft. Inevitably, some bombers will leak through the defense net. It is for this reason that the United States needs a strong home defense as distinguished from a military defense.

Home defense, in my opinion, should focus upon protecting three vital elements in our national economy. First, there is the all-important "nation brain" and "nerve center" which consists of the essential parts of our government without which the country would run out of control like a ship without a rudder. Most governmental function concentrates in Washington, D. C., and steps must be taken to break up this concentration into smaller less vulnerable parts. This we call decentralization. Second, there is the production front made up of thousands of industrial plants many of which concentrate in a few target areas. This industrial concentration, believe it or not, has actually increased since the war so that today our industrial vulnerability is about 20 per cent higher than it was on V-J Day. This dangerous concentration might be avoided over a long period of time by relocating industries in non-target areas. We call this dispersion. Finally, there are the huge masses of our population which are crammed into our teeming metropolitan areas. Obviously, people are just as important to the nation as plants, for machines without men are worthless to any war effort. There are basically two ways to protect these people. One is to redistribute our population into smaller clusters; this, of course, would take many years at best and may never be accomplished. The other is to arrange for the orderly evacuation of our target cities in time of danger. Many objections can be raised to this latter procedure but no one can deny its effectiveness. I think that very few city dwellers will take their chances with an H-bomb. Knowing that such a weapon simply blots out an entire city, they will flee to the safety of the country. Civil defense should recognize this probability and provide measures to control it rather than to resist it.

Reviewing the highlights of this chapter and noting the ever-increasing destructiveness of man's explosive inventions, the reader may be justified in asking whether man is not getting too smart for his own good. Will not man in tinkering with the inside of the nucleus unloose uncontrollable catastrophe? It is fair to say that scientists in emulating what happens in the center of our sun has gone nature one or two better. Nuclear reactions which take millions of years in our sun have been squeezed into the infinitesimal time span of one-millionth of one second. However, such reactions as take place within the H-bomb are extremely difficult to achieve. They take place only under highly special conditions well calculated by the cold scientific mind. It is highly improbable that an H-bomb would get out of hand and burn up the earth's atmosphere. And even though the force released by the H-weapon is fantastically large it is still comparable with some of nature's violent spectacles—earthquakes and big volcanos. Detonating an H-bomb will not knock the earth out of its time-honored orbit around the sun nor will it convert our planet into a blazing star. As Professor Fermi commented on the H-bomb: "Life may become less happy from now on, but it will not be terminated. We still don't have anything powerful enough to destroy the planet."

6

THE ATOMIC IMPASSE

THE remorseless increase in man's capability of devising new
and more powerful weapons of mass destruction poses such a
threat to the peace of the world than any sane individual will
readily agree that every feasible approach to an international
agreement outlawing the use of these weapons ought to be tried.
That the prevailing climate of hostility between nations scarcely
encourages these efforts should be no reason for a lack of dili-
gence in exploring every possibility for agreement. The issues are
too great, the consequences too catastrophic for man to be de-
flected from seeking a means to end war or at the very least to
ban the use of atomic weapons. Even the most casual reading of
the last chapter should convince anyone of the magnitude of the
threat which A- and H-bombs pose to civilization.

Had the A-bomb and the H-bomb come at a different time in

the history of technology the threat to humanity might not have been so immediate. But these new weapons coincided in time with the advent of high-speed long-range aircraft capable of delivering the bombs from one continent to another. It is the grim fact that atomic weapons can be delivered to their targets that so accentuates the threat of these instruments of mass destruction. The relatively few weapons which must be delivered to an enemy's homeland to achieve serious damage on a national scale compresses the time scale of strategic warfare. Chilling though the prospect may be, it is an undeniable fact that the damage which the Allied Air Force dealt out to Germany throughout three grueling years of air raids can be duplicated in a single night of all-out atomic warfare.

In this chapter we shall note briefly the steps which the United States and the United Nations took in trying to secure international agreement on atomic energy. The presentation will be in the nature of a brief reporting on the developments as they occurred chronologically.

Some thought was given to the problem of atomic control prior to the military use of the bomb against Japan but all of this activity was conducted in secret while the nations of the world were still unaware that atomic energy had made its debut into world affairs. I recall that a group of scientists at the Metallurgical Laboratory used to meet in a physics classroom inside the guarded area on the University of Chicago campus. Even before the first bomb was tested at Alamogordo atomic scientists were so sure of the results that some of them turned to thinking about the consequences of letting loose atomic energy into a war-torn world. As I recall a meeting one warm June night in 1945 Dr. Leo Szilard advanced certain proposals dealing with the problem of international control. It seems to me that these informal get-togethers of atomic scientists paved the way for the establishment of the *Bulletin of the Atomic Scientists*. The latter became the closest approximation to a guide to atomic scientists' thinking about atomic energy in all of its phases.

On August 6, 1945, President Truman announced the use of the A-bomb against Japan and concluded his statement with the words:

I shall recommend that the Congress of the United States consider promptly the establishment of an appropriate commission to control the production and use of atomic power within the United States. I shall give further consideration and make further recommendations to the Congress as to how atomic power can become a powerful and forceful influence toward the maintenance of world peace.

As we know now the first recommendation led to the establishment of the Atomic Energy Commission in the United States.

Two months after his epoch-making disclosure of the A-bomb, President Truman followed up his initial statement on seeking international agreement with a message to the Congress in which he said:

The hope of civilization lies in international arrangements looking, if possible, to the renunciation of the use and development of the atomic bomb, and directing and encouraging the use of atomic energy and all future scientific information toward peaceful and humanitarian ends. . . . I therefore propose to initiate discussions first with our associates in this discovery, Great Britain and Canada, and then with other nations, in an effort to effect agreement on the conditions under which co-operation might replace rivalry in the field of atomic power.

It was clear that at this time when the United Nations Organization was not a functioning body the President appreciated the urgency of reaching international agreement and thus took the interim step of calling a three-power conference.

The Prime Ministers of the United Kingdom and Canada met with President Truman in November, 1945, and in what has been called the Truman-Attlee-King declaration set forth the views and objectives of the three nations which had co-operated to develop the A-bomb. It was agreed that a recommendation should be made to the United Nations for the establishment of a U.N. Commission on Atomic Energy so that recommendations on atomic control might be prepared and duly submitted to the parent body. The Commission would be expected to draw up special proposals embracing three major points:

(a) the control of atomic energy to the extent necessary to insure its use only for peaceful purposes.

(b) the elimination from national armaments of atomic weapons and of all other major weapons adaptable to mass destruction.

(c) effective safeguards by way of inspection and other means to protect complying states against the hazards of violations and evasions.

The three-power declaration contained an appraisal of the overwhelming problems presented in the control of atomic energy but rather than try to summarize the formal language of the document we can refer to Senator Arthur H. Vandenberg's summary of the situation confronting the United Nations. This took the form of a letter written to his family pastor just before the Truman-Attlee-King meeting:

I am frank to say that I do not yet know what the answer is to the awful problem which we have brought upon ourselves. It seems perfectly clear that we could not hope to monopolize this secret very long. It also seems clear that atomic energy will have to be put under ultimate international control. This would obviously require a complete and absolute right of world-wide inspection and information. . . . On the other hand, even if we can get complete and adequate international inspection we shall be at the mercy of any brutal aggressor who may suddenly decide to use the atomic bomb against us. So the prospectus is appalling under *any* circumstances and under *any* controls which we might conjure. I sometimes wonder whether the wit of man is competent to deal with this murderous discovery.

What the late Senator Vandenberg appreciated so keenly about the atomic problem was slow in being absorbed by many of his colleagues and by men the world over. Lack of appreciation of the new force can be understood for its very magnitude staggered the imagination. Man was suddenly confronted with a force a million fold more potent than gun powder and his mind reflected off rather than penetrating into the issues raised by the atom. Furthermore, atomic energy was a subject new to almost everyone except scientists; it had its own language and peculiar technology which formed a tough enamel that prevented understanding. Then, too, atomic energy was a dual force. The selfsame material which could be used in a bomb to blow a city to kingdom come could also be used in atomic power plants to generate electricity and be of constructive use to man.

This point about the dual-purpose nature of uranium was one that was very difficult to put across to an audience. In lectures to the public I always allowed time for a question period and from the nature of the queries which were made I knew that a single lecture could never encompass all the aspects of the issues raised by atomic energy. Time was needed for the public to gain a foothold of understanding. Time was also needed for atomic power plants to be built so that atomic power would be a reality and not just something reserved for the indefinite future.

Perhaps this is the best time to pinpoint the dilemma presented by the dual nature of atomic fuel. The real problem in international control of atomic energy is the hazard of U-235 or plutonium stocks which might be in existence for they could relatively quickly be converted into atomic bombs. If one had only to deal with atomic energy as a destructive force the problem would be much simpler because then one could prohibit the manufacture of U-235 or plutonium and inaugurate an inspection and control system which would ferret out any authorized or clandestine production of the material. But if atomic fuels are to be allowed above ground and used extensively for atomic power plants you are playing with lightning. At any moment any potential aggressor might convert his atomic fuel into A-bombs either by diverting it from the power plant or by juggling his books so that he accumulated an unauthorized stockpile of the bomb material. Here then was the dilemma; if the atom was to be used for generating peacetime power it would always be a nightmare since it could also be quickly adapted to bomb use. This situation led some individuals like James B. Conant, president of Harvard University, to make the extreme proposal that we forgo the peacetime benefits of atomic power and prohibit the production of fissionable material.

Conant's suggestion that we turn our back to atomic power cannot be dismissed lightly. The fundamental issue involved is the peace of the world and nothing can be more important than that. For the cause of peace we should be willing to make extreme sacrifices even to the extent that we deprive ourselves of certain advantages which would accrue from atomic power. Of course, it can be argued that we are thus in a position of giving up modern technology and we are trying to do the impossible—to stay the hands of the clock of progress. What Dr. Conant proposed is that we solve our atomic control problem by destroying existing stocks of bomb material and by keeping uranium buried in the earth's surface. This, in effect, would be as Conant put it: "Putting the Genii back in the bottle."

The foregoing developments, slightly out of our chronological sequence, illustrate the many-sided difficulties of the problem of atomic control. We now resume our reporting of the struggle toward international control.

Following the Washington conference and the Truman-Attlee-King declaration, the Foreign Ministers of the Soviet Union, the United States, and the United Kingdom met in Moscow during the Christmas season of 1945. The proposals of the Washington meeting served as a basis for discussion. With some amendments offered by the Soviet Union these were approved and it was agreed that a resolution would be sponsored recommending that the United Nations form an Atomic Energy Commission consisting essentially of eleven members of the U.N. Security Council. On January 24, 1946, the General Assembly of the U.N. unanimously adopted this resolution and the new Commission was established.

This much having been accomplished, the United States set out to explore in detail the nature of the safeguards which would have to be instituted to make sure that atomic weapons were kept under control. Accordingly, two groups of men were convened to prepare a report which would serve both as an advisory for the President in determining national policy and as a working paper for the U.S. representatives on the U.N. Commission. Dean Acheson, then undersecretary of State, was selected as chairman of a committee composed of Mr. John J. McCloy, Dr. James B. Conant, Dr. Vannevar Bush, and Major General L. R. Groves. A Board of Consultants was established with David E. Lilienthal, then chairman of TVA, to head up a group including Mr. Chester I. Barnard, Dr. J. Robert Oppenheimer, Dr. Charles A. Thomas, and Dr. Harry A. Winne.

Members of these two groups steeped themselves in the lore

of atomic energy by discussions across the conference table and by firsthand experience gained in visiting Oak Ridge, Los Alamos, and other atomic installations. At the outset they recognized both the gravity of the problem they attacked and the difficulty of its solution. The problem was more than technical or scientific; it was deeply rooted in a complex of social, political, and administrative factors. After many weeks of deliberations the two groups published their findings under the title *A Report on the International Control of Atomic Energy*, more popularly known as the Acheson-Lilienthal report. Although later modified, this report formed the substantial basis for the United States proposals on the control of atomic energy; it defined the position which this nation was to take throughout the many months of debate in the United Nations.

Those who wrote the report adopted a realistic attitude toward the problem of control through inspection as is documented by a single quotation: "We have concluded unanimously that there is no prospect of security against atomic warfare in a system of international agreements to outlaw such weapons controlled *only* by a system which relies on inspection and similar police-like methods." Acknowledging that any effective action toward securing an atomic peace must inevitably be novel and immensely difficult the advisors recommended a bold stroke. They recommended international ownership and administration of all "dangerous" atomic activities by an Atomic Development Authority.

The report divided atomic activities into two categories— those which it regarded as "dangerous" and those which were judged to be "safe." Dangerous activities included (a) the provision of raw materials such as uranium, (b) the processing of these raw materials to provide bomb materials, and (c) the fabrication of atomic weapons. Under the category of "safe" were listed such activities as the production and use of radio-isotopes, the development and operation of small research reactors, and the development of power from A-power plants run on "denatured" atomic fuel. Such safe activities could be indulged in by individual nations and would not be included within the monopoly of the Atomic Development Authority. The term "denatured" requires both explanation and comment. It was proposed that both U-235 and plutonium which are useful in atomic weapons could be altered by adding an adulterant to them so that they would be unfit for A-weapon use but would still be useful for fueling A-power plants. In the light of present knowledge it no longer appears that "denaturing" holds much promise and although it might make a system of control more flexible it would not eliminate the possibility of converting the material into bomb material.

Finally, the report specified that the transfer of bomb material and plant facilities to the custody of the Atomic Development Authority would be a gradual one. To cushion a nation against the shock of yielding a cherished possession to the ownership and management of an international authority several stages were delineated for the actual transfer process.

Bernard Baruch meanwhile had been appointed by the President to be the U.S. representative to the U.N. Atomic Energy Commission. In addressing the first session of this Commission, Mr. Baruch stated: "We are here to make a choice between the quick and the dead. That is our business." He then spelled out the U. S. proposals which were essentially those contained in the Acheson-Lilienthal Report with but two major exceptions. First, there must be severe penalties meted out to any nation violating the international agreement or, as Bernard Baruch put it, there must be "an international law with teeth in it." Second, and again in Mr. Baruch's language, "there must be no veto to protect those who violate their solemn agreements not to develop or use atomic energy for destructive purposes." He added: "The bomb does not wait upon debate. To delay may be to die." The Charter of the U.N. provided that sanctions could be invoked only if the five permanent members of the Security Council concurred. The latter included China, France, the Soviet Union, the United Kingdom, and the United States.

The United States was offering to make sweeping concessions in the cause of world peace. If an adequate atomic control system could be implemented the United States proposed to dispose of its atomic weapons, to turn over to international authority its atomic facilities, and to give up what we may broadly call its atomic secrets.

Refraining from making direct comment upon the U.S. proposals, Mr. Gromyko of the Soviet Union countered with two alternative proposals. One stipulated that the U.S.A. must stop making more A-bombs and must destroy existing atomic stockpiles prior to negotiating a control plan. The other called for a "rule of unanimity" in the Security Council which in effect upheld the veto power of a single nation member of the Security Council. Should any permanent member of the Council or friend of that nation employ the veto on invoking sanctions for violating the atomic agreement then the U.N. would be powerless to deal with the aggressor nation.

The Baruch proposals won the support of the majority of the member nations of the U.N. and became known by the title "the Majority Plan." Russia stood firm on its stand on international ownership and management and on the veto issue. On the question of international inspection the Soviets made a partial concession, agreeing to periodic inspection of facilities for mining and production of atomic materials with the proviso that inspectors would visit only *declared* plants. It was evident that the Soviets had little enthusiasm for inspectors roaming freely behind the Iron Curtain and they considered that such action would be a severe infringement of the sovereignty of the U.S.S.R. However, such partial or limited inspection of such areas as the Russians permitted was an insufficient guarantee against unauthorized atomic activities.

Throughout the long-drawn-out committee meetings which took place during the next several years the representatives of the Soviet Union retreated only slightly from their original position. They intimated that Russia would agree to back down from its stand on the banning of atomic weapons prior to discussing the control plan. Ground was also apparently yielded on the matter of inspection when Russia made the concession that it would agree to a rather rigid inspection system including provision for special investigations where the control authority had reason to believe violations were being perpetrated. Unfortunately, these concessions were made late in the game. Had they come earlier they might have buoyed up hope that the Majority Plan would gain acceptance in the U.N. Coming as they did after Russia had perfected its own atomic weapons and after much evasiveness on the part of the U.S.S.R. in U.N. negotiations no one could be sure whether the concessions were bona fide or sham. On the point of agreeing to international ownership of atomic facilities the position taken by the Soviet Union was adamant and did not change throughout six years of negotiation. Speaking to the issue in 1952 Jacob Malik charged that the idea of such ownership—a keystone in the Majority Plan—was a plot by United States monopolists to establish "an atomic supertrust" to grab control of the world's atomic potential. The Soviet

Deputy Foreign Minister made it perfectly clear that until such plans for international ownership were abandoned there was little point in planning an international inspection scheme.

The testing of the first Soviet A-bomb in the late summer of 1949 touched off the present atomic arms race between the U.S.A. and the U.S.S.R. It is known that the Soviets are making feverish efforts to increase their own atomic production in order to make up for the disparity between their small stockpile and the much larger one of the United States. The accumulation of large quantities of bomb material behind the Iron Curtain introduces the factor that both sides must trust each other in declaring the amounts of atomic material stockpiled prior to international agreement. To a certain extent the production capacities of atomic plants would reveal the true accumulated stockpile but some diversion and secretion of bomb material might be possible. In a sense this very fact simplifies the problem because one no longer needs to worry about making an absolutely leakproof inspection and control system for post-agreement production. It does, however, place a strain upon the willingness of each nation to believe each other's declared stockpile figures. This tension might be relieved by agreement on a complete and drastic inspection system.

Four years after the establishment of the U.N. Atomic Energy Commission representatives of Russia withdrew from discussions on the atomic control question over the issue of U.N. recognition of the Chinese Communist government. At this time the relative positions of Russia and the United States were still along the lines drawn in the Majority Plan which had been approved in 1948 by the U.N. General Assembly by a vote of forty to six. Incidentally, it is significant that this plan was never presented to the Russian people through the medium of the Kremlin-controlled press. Thus after endless hours of debate, of proposal and counterproposal, atomic negotiations within the framework of the U.N. structure had apparently reached a dead end. The West awaited the next move from the Soviets and hoped that somehow the atomic impasse would be resolved.

Foreign Minister Andrei Y. Vishinsky made the next step. On November 16, 1951, he presented a new disarmament plan to the U.N. General Assembly calling for an arms reduction. This proposal tied in with the Soviet theme that atomic and conventional arms constitute a single problem. During the following winter the U.N. discussions focused on the disarmament issue and in the first month of 1952 the U.N. set up a new Disarmament Commission. Mr. Vishinsky promptly stepped forward and dramatically scored a propaganda victory in introducing a resolution that the newly created Commission should consider both the disarmament and atomic problem. In presenting the resolution the Soviet Foreign Minister claimed that his country was making two major concessions. First, it agreed that prohibition of atomic weapons should not come before institution of proper atomic controls but should occur simultaneously. Second, continuous inspection of atomic facilities would be permitted; previously the Soviet position had been that only periodic and announced visits of international inspectors would be allowed. Barring the possibility that these two concessions would later be repudiated, it would appear that there was room for cautious optimism. However, Soviet statements on atomic energy in the past had been transparent propaganda. Vishinsky, in addressing the United Nations General Assembly, had stated:

We, in the Soviet Union, are using atomic energy not for the stockpiling of atomic bombs. . . . We have set atomic energy to perform great tasks of peaceful construction, we want to put atomic energy to use in leveling mountains, changing the course of rivers, watering deserts, and laying new life lines in places where the foot of man has rarely stepped. This is what we, the masters of our land, are doing, under our plan, and we shall not in this matter subordinate ourselves or render account to any international agencies.

Soviet representatives have never given any indication of wavering on the stand taken on international ownership of atomic plants. The latter is the core of the problem and unless agreement on this crucial point can be reached it would seem that atomic control is doomed to more years of fruitless discussions.

If the Soviets were to agree in principle with sacrificing national control of their atomic facilities there is the practical matter of the mechanism for declaring and turning these over to the international authority. According to a United States working paper prepared in April of 1952 atomic disarmament would be a part of a general disarmament which would follow a world arms census. Such a census would presumably take about two years and it would be a graduated arms count spread over five stages. The first stage would pertain to manpower strengths in the armed services and location of operational military installations. Disclosures and verifications of military strength would proceed from Stage 1 through Stage 5, the latter being a disclosure of novel weapons such as atomic and bacteriological arms and a verification by count of the quantities of these weapons in stockpile. By making the arms census in a series of steps it is reasoned that confidence between nations could be built up to a point where the countries would permit inspection of atomic vaults.

Certainly, an arms census would constitute a big step forward in any disarmament plan but there would be two big obstacles remaining. Agreement would have to be reached on the numbers of each type of weapon which would be permitted to remain in the custody of each nation. Somehow decision would have to be reached on the question of how many planes, tanks, and bombs Russia, Great Britain, the United States, and other nations could retain in its possession. The Acheson-Lilienthal report had advanced the concept of strategic balance in the disposition of atomic plants and stockpiles, but this proposition was rejected by the Soviets. Basically, the idea underlying strategic balance is that if war breaks out then any single nation will still be in a relatively secure position as compared to any other nation. At the present stage of the atomic arms race it is difficult to see how the concept of strategic balance can be implemented. The United States has built up a vast atomic industry with a huge stockpile of atomic weapons. Russia on the other hand now has a smaller stockpile. Striking a strategic balance so as to annul this disparity would seem exceeding difficult. One has further to consider what strategic balance means once several countries each accumulates enough A-bombs to deal lethal destruction to another nation. Should this problem be resolved there would remain the practical matter of putting the international authority in business and merging the atomic facilities of many nations. Proposals have been made that this might be accomplished on a step-by-step basis with each nation relinquishing a certain fraction of its facilities and stockpile in say three months, another fraction in the next three months, and so on until the international merger would have been completed.

As the year 1952 took America into its tenth year of the Atomic Age, scientists in the United States urged that a fresh approach be tried to see if the atomic deadlock could not be resolved. Scientists who had ushered in the Atomic Age saw just below the horizon superweapons like the hydrogen bomb and they knew that this would in Soviet hands tend to accelerate the arms race and in fact give an advantage to Russia. They saw a world which was rapidly becoming overcritical—a world beyond control—and they argued that every facet of the atomic control problem must again be studied to see if one might reflect a few rays of light to illuminate the problem. That the international situation had progressively deteriorated and that there seemed not one chance in a thousand for agreement on the atomic issue should not, the scientists argued, deter the United States from taking a new look at the problem.

In response to this urging, the State Department early in the summer of 1952 appointed a committee of eminent Americans to reappraise the course of the atomic arms race and the possibilities of new approaches to disarmament and atomic control. Dr. J. Robert Oppenheimer was appointed as chairman. Other members include Dr. Vannevar Bush, President John S. Dickey of Dartmouth, Allen W. Dulles of the Central Intelligence Agency, and Dr. Joseph Johnson, president of the Carnegie Endowment for International Peace. With such a distinguished membership it is to be hoped that a bold new plan for international control of atomic energy will be evolved.

A year before, the United States had announced with considerable fanfare that it would present a bold plan to the U.N. only to cause our Allies to despair when it turned out that the plan was little more than a restatement of previous U.S. proposals. This gave a propaganda advantage to the Soviets who were quick to seize it. At the very least the new Oppenheimer committee can serve to buoy up hope that a really new approach is being made.

In one sense it should be easier for the United States to make further concessions since Russia now has the A-bomb. The gulf between the two nations is thus less than it was before the advent of the Soviet bomb. One can imagine how the U.S. Senate would have viewed turning over the U.S. atomic stockpile and atomic secrets to an international authority when the Soviet Union did not have a single A-bomb. Now at least both of the major disputants have their own stockpiles and their own atomic secrets. Naturally, the Congress will have to be persuaded that it would be in the best national interest to give up the one weapon which it has held was the principal deterrent to Soviet aggression during the postwar years.

If true disarmament can be achieved then one can know a measure of security from the ability to deliver A-weapons rather than from the bombs themselves. For example, should any nation decide to violate the international agreements and use atomic weapons there would be in addition to the time required to fabricate A-bombs the longer time which is required to build substantial numbers of long-range aircraft.

As for the hidden menace of atomic power plants it may be possible to subscribe to the Conant thesis that the benefits of applied atomic power can be forgone. Man has yet to directly benefit from this new power source and if it poses such a serious threat to humanity perhaps it can be abandoned in the interests of world peace.

On the issue of international ownership of atomic facilities it is not impossible that the United States would agree to this proposal being compromised. Reliance would have to be placed upon international inspection rather than upon ownership, and while the less satisfactory of the two, it might have to do.

It may be that atomic agreement is not possible. Or it may be that the chance of agreement is vanishingly small. Whatever the prospects there is clearly the responsibility for the United States to explore within the framework of the United Nations every nook and cranny of the problem. It must be indelibly engraved into the record that the United States did not forsake its responsibilities in the area of world peace. The alternative to international agreement on atomic energy is terrible to contemplate. It is a world filled with the potential of mutual extinction. When more than one nation possesses the strategic capability of launching a blitz attack upon another's homeland peace will be a precarious business. Perhaps, like two beasts of the jungle that respect each other's fangs there might be an avoidance of a cataclysmic encounter, each knowing the risk he ran, but perhaps the urge to be king of the jungle would be overwhelming, the prize overshadowing the risk. In any event a peace between fully armed nations would represent a highly unstable equilibrium condition. The sheer explosive content of the situation would argue against any permanence.

All of this results from the untimely advent of the Atomic Age. The new force is still too new and too unappreciated for the peoples of the world to sense its true meaning for mankind. Tens of thousands of years ago when a chance lightning stroke ushered in the Age of Fire for man he dealt on a very small scale with a blessing and a curse. Even today we have trouble keeping fire in check so that it does not destroy our homes and our factories. Gradually, by trial and error, man has learned to adopt certain safeguards in dealing with fire so that it is his servant and not his master.

Man is now called upon to bring into being much more drastic safeguards to curb the potential violence of the atom. Perhaps these safeguards, as in the case of fire, will have to originate on a trial and error basis but it is so easy to see the results of an atomic war that this should not be necessary. It is imperative to impress upon the mind of man that the real significance of releasing atomic energy is that war must be abolished from this earth.

7

BATTLEFIELD A-WEAPONS

At the time the Acheson-Lilienthal report was written all thinking about atomic weapons focused on the Nagasaki-type A-bombs. These came under the heading of "big A-bombs" or of strategic weapons designed for bombardment of an enemy's homeland. The weapons were estimated to weigh about five tons and only B-29 bombers were capable of delivering them. Apparently little thought was given to making smaller, lighter, less powerful atomic weapons for tactical use—that is, for use on the battlefield or in support of ground warfare.

Of course, the Nagasaki bomb could have been dropped at the front lines by a strategic bomber but military planners did not regard this weapon as suited for tactical employment. To be truly a tactical weapon the A-bomb had to be converted into a bomb small enough to be carried by tactical aircraft or fired as a shell.

This development was not initially viewed with great enthusiasm by most of the Air Force for it meant that the A-bomb could then also be delivered by the Navy's carrier-based aircraft. Some Air Force officers naturally championed land-based aircraft for strategic bombing. There thus ensued a bitter Air Force-Navy row over the development of a tactical A-bomb. This head-on clash between the two services served to delay the advent of smaller nuclear weapons.

There were, in addition, other factors which stymied work on cutting the atomic weapon down to size so that it would become a useful battlefield explosive. All weapon development slowed down after V-J day and the atomic bomb work at the Los Alamos laboratory of the Atomic Energy Commission was no exception. Two years were to elapse before the newly established Atomic Energy Commission could infuse the breath of life into its Los Alamos weapons center. Those scientists and weapons experts who remained on the job seem to have been peculiarly fascinated by the lure of bigger A-bombs and blind to the need for smaller weapons.

In defense of those in charge of U.S. weapon development it may be said that the argument was not completely black and white. A shade of gray was introduced by a technical-economic factor. As long as the supply of U-235 and Pu-239 was strictly limited and in short supply as it was in the early postwar years it was imperative that this precious material be conserved. Another way of saying the same thing more graphically is that it would be almost sinful to waste any of the explosive power of the bomb material. And it appeared then that if you made the A-bomb smaller you did not use the U-235 or Pu-239 as efficiently. For example, the Nagasaki bomb yielded an explosive equivalent of 20,000 tons of T.N.T. Making this bomb smaller but using the same amount of Pu-239 might mean getting only a 5,000 ton explosion. This, in effect, would be like going to a bank and exchanging all your dollar bills for an equal number of quarters. Military men, especially in the Air Force, maintained that it was essential to get a high return for a given investment in fissionable material. Therefore, highest priority was assigned by the Joint Chiefs of Staff to the stockpiling of big strategic A-bombs and to developing even bigger ones. There is little doubt but that the policy of stockpiling such weapons was sound but this should not have interfered with research and development on smaller A-weapons.

The Navy did not meekly accept the Air Force proprietorship of the A-bomb. Even though it could not persuade others in the National Military Establishment to agree to transmitting a formal military requirement for smaller A-weapons to the AEC, the Navy did persuade some scientists at Los Alamos to conduct exploratory investigations in new A-weapons which might be light enough to fit into the bomb bays of carrier-aircraft. Due largely to this Navy stimulus the AEC was ready to launch a large-scale program on making tactical weapons when the Joint Chiefs of Staff finally agreed upon a requirement for smaller bombs.

While the Navy was fighting its battle with the Air Force the Army more or less sat in a corner resigned to a nonatomic role in military weaponry. In part this could be explained by the fact that within the Army atomic energy was a closely held activity confined to a small clique of officers. All atomic matters were held so secret that the rank and file of Army officers who should have been active in planning the use of A-weapons were excluded from getting atomic data. This situation persisted for about four years following the end of the war. However, as events developed on the world scene it became evident that the

Army would still be called upon to play a major role in any future war. While the strategic striking power of the Air Force might continue to deter the Soviets from launching a war in Europe one could not depend upon it. Furthermore, once war broke out all the strategic A-bombs in the world, rained down upon Soviet cities, factories, oil wells, and other strategic targets, might not stop the Red Army from racing across Europe to the Channel.

The overwhelming troop superiority of the Soviet Union jeopardized the security of Western Europe. No means seemed in sight to oppose the crushing weight of Red divisions with Allied ground forces in comparable number. Lacking the man power the military leaders in the United States decided to employ weapon power against the threat of the Red Army. It was only natural to turn to the most potent of all weapons and to adapt it to the battlefield. Emphasis was therefore placed upon the development of smaller-lighter A-weapons which might be used tactically to ward off the threat of Communist aggression. Maximum priority was assigned to the task of making the bomb small enough to be carried by a jet fighter such as the Air Force's F-84. Presumably, this meant trimming down the Nagasaki weapon to less than two tons in weight.

Second priority was attached to a much tougher assignment, namely, to developing an atomic artillery shell. Squeezing down the size and weight of the A-bomb so that it could fit into a gun barrel was truly a formidable task. The gadget had to be rugged enough to withstand being fired at high velocity from the gun barrel. Just the size limitations alone constituted an intricate problem for the shell had to be made to fit a mobile gun and this meant that it had to be of the order of a foot in diameter since larger bore howitzers could not be made readily mobile. Thus the atomic problem was essentially one of making a shell which would fit a naval-type gun capable of firing one-ton projectiles from fifteen to twenty-two miles with good accuracy. This part of the task went to the Atomic Energy Commission and the more conventional assignment of making the gun went to Army Ordnance.

Priority was also assigned to fabricating an A-bomb to fit into a guided missile as an atomic warhead. This was a somewhat easier problem technically because the bulk of the warhead could be larger than for an artillery shell. Furthermore, since guided missiles did not promise to become truly operational until 1954 or later there was less urgency as to the time for developing the warheads.

We shall discuss these three atomic gadgets in more detail after noting that they had their technical origin in the atomic bombs tests which the Atomic Energy Commission started in the spring of 1951. The test program for smaller atomic weapons was rapidly accelerated by the outbreak of the Korean War as the summer of 1950 began. It would, however, have been severely hampered if the A-tests had been relegated to the Eniwetok Proving Grounds. Officialdom in Washington had decreed that no A-bombs would be tested within the continental limits of the United States but the emergency of the Korean War set aside this ruling. A new atomic proving grounds was set up in Nevada some seventy miles from Las Vegas.

Even before the first new weapon or weapon prototype was tested at the new proving grounds the Pentagon jumped the gun by releasing the news about atomic artillery. This unusual policy whereby the military publicize their new weapons while still in the embryo stage is difficult to understand. For one thing it produces at home severe misconceptions as to the rate at which new weapons are being developed. In the case of atomic artillery it took well over two years for the weapon to come into being after it had been disclosed by General J. Lawton Collins in 1950.

An even dozen "nuclear devices" as the AEC prefers to describe its Nevada-type bombs were detonated in 1951 and more nuclear weapon prototypes were exploded in subsequent series of A-tests in 1952. It is to be expected that many more bombs will be tested in 1953 and in following years. Most of the bombs tested have been of the small size or less than 20,000 tons of T.N.T. in their explosive impact. At first the rather profligate detonation of U-235 alarmed the press and led to many wild conclusions as to the results of the tests in Nevada. Without going into the intimate technology of atomic weapons the test results can be summarized as follows:

(a) The over-all physical size and weight of the A-bomb has been significantly reduced. But talk of "baby" A-bombs or atomic hand grenades belongs in the realm of science fiction.

(b) Smaller atomic explosions, less than the equivalent of 20,000 tons of T.N.T., have been produced. However, detonations must still be measured in terms of thousands of tons of T.N.T.

(c) Making the bomb smaller involves a definite loss in efficiency or in the percentage burn-up of uranium in the bomb. A very small bomb, such as for firing in an artillery piece, is not as efficient as a larger bomb such as could be dropped from an airplane.

Essentially, the Nevada tests have paved the way for a "family of atomic weapons" ranging from a bomb which can be used in tactical aircraft to one which could be fitted as a warhead to a guided missile. In this small family of weapons the prototype of an atomic artillery shell was tested.

Making the A-shell was a technical achievement which some

bomb experts had felt would not be possible. Making the A-gun or the big atomic howitzer to fire the atomic projectile was mostly an engineering development, for big guns had been made before. It was largely a question of making the high caliber howitzer light enough to be transported quickly. The Army Ordnance Department had set to work designing a big mobile gun after the last war. This howitzer was to fire ordinary high explosive shells to be used for siege reduction purposes against strongly fortified enemy positions. When the possibility of atomic shells came up the gun was adapted to fire both ordinary and atomic projectiles.

The atomic howitzer was officially announced on May 8, 1952, by Frank Pace, the Secretary of Army. He described it in these words: "It is essentially an artillery piece. Carried on a platform suspended between two engine cabs at front and rear [it] can travel at a speed of thirty-five miles per hour on highways." Other data about the new gun include the fact that it has a total weight of seventy-five tons including the cannon, its mount, and the two tank retrievers which move it about. This large weight puts a limitation on its battlefield utility since it could not be trundled across most long-span bridges. Its total dinosaur proportions make it a standout on the battlefield and render it a target for enemy counteraction. However, it has the capability of projecting a shell more than fifteen miles with quite high accuracy—this will be of value against massive concrete fortifications where pinpoint accuracy may be needed even with A-shells. Despite the fact that the A-gun is less flexible in covering large stretches of the front line than is tactical aircraft, Army generals feel that it has several advantages which will make it a valuable battlefield asset.

First, the atomic artillery post can be swiftly co-ordinated with the front-line commander. The importance of this point will be developed shortly. Second, the A-gun can fire in any kind of weather when aircraft might be grounded and be unable to deliver the required A-weapon. Third, the A-shell can be used with high accuracy; this is important because the large radius of lethal action of the A-explosive might overlap friendly troop positions if good accuracy in delivery were not achieved. Finally, the A-gun can be used even if the enemy has command of the air. Air Force officers dispute the latter claim since they feel that the A-gun is an easy target for enemy aircraft. At any rate, the Air Force would prefer to retain cognizance for delivery of tactical weapons under its own wing. Since no large numbers of A-guns have been produced or made operational it is clear that the Air Force will have primary responsibility for delivering A-weapons on the battlefield up through the period 1954. After that time it is expected that the guided missile will become operational and will at first supplement the aerial delivery of A-weapons and then substitute for it. The Army is spending vast sums on developing guided missiles for A-warheads, far more than it set aside for developing atomic artillery. It may therefore be inferred that the Army regards A-guns under the category of interim weapons and will shift emphasis to guided missiles when they become available.

Although A-weapons for tactical use come in assorted sizes which are measured in kilotons of T.N.T. equivalent it is useful for purposes of discussing the effect of the weapon on the battlefield to fix attention upon a 10 kt bomb. That is one which is equivalent to 10,000 tons of T.N.T. or is one half as powerful as the Nagasaki bomb. Smaller weapons are possible but would be expected to be less efficient in using the bomb material; therefore, as long as the bomb stockpile is a significant factor, such

smaller weapons would be warranted only for special purposes—
for example, in penetrating A-shells. When we come to specify-
ing just what damage a 10 kt A-bomb explosion will do on the
battlefield the problem is much more difficult than predicting
what the same explosion would do against buildings. The casualty and mortality data about the A-bomb have been derived
from results at Hiroshima and Nagasaki. In these two Japanese
cities people were injured by a multiplicity of effects so that it is
not possible to separate out casualties due to the direct heat,
radiation, and blast of the explosion and the secondary effects
due to shattered window glass, falling beams, flying debris, and
secondary fires.

As between people concentrated in a city and soldiers spread
out on the battlefield it is clear that in general only the primary
heat flash, the first flash of penetrating radiation, and the blast
wave may be effective in causing battlefield casualties. Soldiers
close in when the A-bomb explodes over them, say, within ¾
mile, will have a very small chance of survival *if* they are standing up in the open—utterly unprotected. Beyond this distance
an unprotected soldier would have increasing chance of escaping
harm up to a distance of 1¼ miles where he would be safe, especially if he ducked and sought cover as he would be trained to do.
Lethal penetrating radiation would be confined to a ¾ mile
radius. The terrific blast effect of the bomb would not cause
many deaths beyond this distance principally because a human
being can absorb terrible punishment from blast pressure and still
survive. Unlike a building which is relatively fragile and fixed
immovably to the ground, a person is relatively tough and can
roll with the punch. Soldiers may be knocked off their feet
by the blast wave but except close in, this will not produce many
serious injuries. The farthest felt effect of the bomb will be from
the heat flash; this is also the one most difficult to avoid. Depend-

ing upon the clarity of the atmosphere serious burns could be produced out to a radius of 1¼ miles. Soldiers trained to duck and take instant evasive action could cover their exposed parts and avoid skin burns. Even though clothing might be scorched and flames kindled these could be beaten out without difficulty. All in all it would seem that a city dweller stands in more danger from the bomb than does a soldier at the front line—at least as we have stated the situation here.

Soldiers who are protected by even such a rudimentary shelter as a slit trench or a foxhole can survive A-bombs even though they are exploded close by. As a rule of thumb anyone in a good foxhole at 1 mile from the burst would be quite safe, probably also safe at ¾ mile, and possibly at ½ mile. So the old slogan that a foxhole is a soldier's best friend holds even in the age of battlefield A-bombs. Clearly, if A-bombs are to be used with maximum effectiveness, they must catch an enemy unaware and unprotected.

But, while going underground may be an effective way for a soldier to survive even A-bombs, it is no way to win battles. To win, ground soldiers must get up out of their foxholes and occupy enemy territory. Once out of the foxhole they are vulnerable to atomic attack. This illustrates the point that use of the A-bomb may require delicate timing on the part of the user if he is to catch an enemy in a vulnerable attitude. Such precise timing may be exceedingly difficult when one considers the over-all problem which faces a commander in employing an A-bomb on the battlefield.

The reader may find it useful to consider that he is a front-line commander and is the one responsible for giving the order to use an A-bomb against an enemy attack. Here are the links in the chain of factors which you would have to consider.

First would be the all-important element of accurate and up-to-date intelligence data. Suppose that you thought the enemy had concentrated a full division along your sector. Before you would think of using an A-bomb you would have to be sure that this was actually true. Yet, accurate battlefield intelligence, as any veteran of the front lines will tell you, is hard to get. Furthermore, it is next to impossible under bad weather conditions or in difficult terrain. Added to this would be the possibility that your enemy might be fully aware you contemplated using an A-bomb and might have some tricks up his sleeve to delude you into using the bomb too soon or under conditions which would make for a poor target.

Next, with the intelligence data at hand and assuming it to be good, you would have the problem of evaluating whether or not you had a good atomic target in front of you. In cold-blooded terms you would have to ask yourself the question: "Is the target worth an A-bomb?" Naturally, your decision would depend upon a complex of things such as how precarious your position was, how many A-bombs were at your disposal, the nature of the terrain, the degree to which the enemy had dug-in, and how close his front line was to yours. The latter point may be very significant for if the enemy is too close you may not be able to use a bomb without exposing your own men to atomic fire. So in a sense your A-bomb would be too big a weapon for your own good. But assuming that everything added up to a good target for an A-bomb you would need to consider still another factor, the bomb delivery.

With the decision made to use the bomb it would be a question of delivering the weapon where you wanted it when you wanted it. Timing would be very important to nip an enemy attack in the bud. Too early an explosion might find the enemy still dug in and protected; too late an attack might find the enemy above ground but too close for proper use of the weapon. This situation points up the Army claim that it must have guaranteed split-second delivery of the weapon. Such delivery, the Army claims, is achieved only via atomic artillery or atomic missiles. Delivery via a tactical airplane may be possible but the timing would be much more difficult to control.

The combination of these three major factors—intelligence, assurance of a proper target, and timing in delivery—adds up to the fact that proper use of the new weapon will require great skill and finesse. However, skillful employment of tactical atomic weapons may stop an enemy dead in his tracks. The prime significance of the new weapon is that the age-old pattern of massing men to break through enemy defenses is no longer possible or can be undertaken only on a sudden-death-risk basis. Once an enemy makes the mistake of concentrating men and material in a few-square-mile area he has formed a target for an A-bomb.

The penalty levied by the tactical atomic weapon can be appreciated by comparing the damage with that produced by massed artillery fire. In making such a comparison it is easy to arrive at very misleading results. For example, the layman might immediately conclude that one A-bomb of the 10 kt type is equal to 10,000 tons of artillery shells laid down in a barrage over the same area hit by the atomic explosion. This is grossly untrue. In the first place the atomic explosion equals 10,000 tons of T.N.T. only when the latter is stacked up in one pile and then detonated simultaneously. Distributing the T.N.T. in one-ton stacks over the stricken area calls for only about 1,000 tons of the material to give the same explosive effect. This is because one big punch at the center just cannot do the damage that a thousand smaller punches produce over the same area. If we focus attention on the 155 mm artillery—the famous Long Tom guns—we can appreciate that such field pieces need not distribute their fire over, say, three square miles uniformly. They can be accurately aimed to fire at targets within the area. These and still other factors show that one A-bomb is roughly the equal of 4,000 rounds of shells slammed home by the 155 mm guns. It would take 4,000 Long Tom guns to deliver these shells simultaneously on target, but if we consider an hour-long artillery barrage, about 100 guns would be required. Thus one A-weapon substitutes for the concentration fire of massed artillery and it spells superfire power for the user.

In the face of such fire power even the most ancient and honored military practices require drastic revision if an army is to survive on the field of battle. Army leaders must pore over their battle plans like ardent chess fans scrutinizing every square mile of the battle area to make sure that no critical point is exposed to the lethal lash of the atom. Brute force concentration of man power or tanks or guns must be avoided.

The alternative to concentration is dispersion. By spreading troops and equipment over an extended front you present a much poorer target to an atomic attack. General Bradley illustrated the point in a Congressional hearing when he stated: "If you did not oppose them the Russians could walk across Europe at 100-yard intervals, and walk all the way to the Channel, and you would never get an A-bomb target." What this means is that the atom alone cannot stop an attack by the ground forces. Dispersion of an attacking force would neutralize the defensive power if it were based solely on a stockpile of A-weapons. The defense must be doubly armed. It must have conventional strength in soldiers, guns, tanks, and planes to turn back a dispersed attack. And it must have atomic striking power to stop the sheer massed force of the enemy. The two go hand in hand, for soldiers manning a strong defensive line can force the enemy to concentrate in order to pierce the line. Once concentration occurs then the A-bomb finds its target. Thus the A-bomb becomes a supplementary weapon which depends upon the existence of a strong conventional defense for setting up the enemy into attractive concentrations which invite atomic attack.

Thus we see that dispersion alone is not the answer to the tactical A-bomb. We have already noted that deception, taking advantage of foul weather or terrain, using the cover of darkness, and arranging the attack in neatly timed successive waves may still allow a concentration attack. However, such operations will be made perilous by the superfire power of the atomic weapon used defensively. As a general rule it would appear that dispersion must be employed on the battlefield. If the principle is adopted then it follows that you automatically lose the advantage of man power superiority unless you provide communications, troop transport, logistics, and battle co-ordination which are better than those of the enemy. Dispersion will be an effective policy only if machines and equipment serve, so to speak, to fill up the gaps between the men on the front line. This, in effect, puts the advantage on the side with the best production line.

Thus the real revolution which the tactical A-weapon will produce is in the nature of a deterrent to concentration. One revolution which has been credited to the new weapon does not now appear to be in the cards—it is the possible use of the A-bomb to deny territory to enemy occupation through radioactive contamination. One Congressman who had apparently been peering over the shoulder of a scientist saw things which were not revealed to the scientist for he published a letter stating that the atom made possible a revolutionary kind of warfare which could deny land to human occupation. Referring to the situation in

Korea, the legislator urged President Truman to authorize the use of the new weapon to lay down a belt of radioactivity, making an uninhabitable strip stretching across the battlefront, thus isolating the Communists and insuring against an attack. This would amount to denial warfare and would immunize front-line troops against attack provided that the enemy could not send his troops across the radioactive no man's land.

Theoretically, the most potent way to lay down radioactive material on the ground would be to detonate an A-bomb well below the surface of the soil. The majority of the fission products produced by the nuclear reaction in the A-bomb would be trapped in the soil. For example, exploding a 10 kiloton A-bomb about fifty feet below the earth's surface creates the maximum blow-out of earth and thus produces the greatest amount of contaminated soil. Detonation of the weapon in this way would blast loose about 2 million tons of soil and rock and would create a crater about 1,200 feet wide and 100 feet deep. Such a deep underground explosion would be a rare military tactic perhaps used only in a superbooby trap operation when ground was to be yielded in retreat. Bombs which would be fused to detonate on contact with the earth's surface or shells which might penetrate farther into the surface would dislodge less soil and would dish out smaller and shallower craters. Calculations show that for a deep underground atomic burst the crater area would be so intensely radioactive that it would be denied to human passage for roughly one hour. During this time anyone traversing the area would be killed by unseen and unfelt radioactive rays. However, time heals all things including radioactivity. Shortly after one hour an infantryman could trot across the crater's rim, avoiding the excavation, and suffer no serious effects. But he could not pitch camp in the hot area or stay there very long, say, in a foxhole. To be more quantitative about the radioactive hazard and the way in which it fades out with time we may state that in the first hour the initial radioactivity decreases 200 fold and one day later it is 10,000 times weaker than just after the explosion. For these reasons experts have concluded that this type of radioactive warfare would have only very limited military application on the battlefield.

No sooner than it had been concluded that denial-type warfare with atomic explosions might be of quite limited military utility than the H-bomb came along. Some military men immediately jumped to the conclusion that the H-bomb, being so much more powerful than the A-weapon, could prove of great tactical value in denial-type warfare. A new concept was advanced in making this proposal. The new idea was to surround the H-weapon with a suitable overcoat of a metal. Then the radiations released in the fusion reaction would make this metal radioactive and this radioactive material would deny many square miles of territory to an enemy. In theory this made up for one deficiency of the A-bomb —its rapid decrease of radioactivity—for by selecting the proper element to be made radioactive it would fade away less rapidly than fission products. However, the very violence of the superbomb makes such radioactive denial impossible. Instead of laying down a fine dust of radioactive particles on the battlefield the explosion sucks up the material in a huge mushroom cloud which is so characteristic of atomic explosions. It acts like a huge vacuum cleaner and scours the earth of the radioactive contamination. This was true of the bombs exploded at Hiroshima, at Eniwetok, and at the Nevada bomb tests.

Inevitably, any discussion of A-bombs and the battlefield gravitates to the question of how many bombs will be needed in a future war. Of course, much will be dependent upon the strategic circumstances of the war so that any quantitative estimate will be meaningless. About all that one can hope to do is to arrive at the order of magnitude of the number, that is, whether it is in the tens, hundreds, or thousands. One way of answering the question might be to try to guess how many battle targets there would be for the new tactical weapons but this is almost like the question: "Which came first, the hen or the egg?" The number of targets will depend upon how many bombs are in the stockpile. If the A-bombs available to a field commander are many then he will be more tempted to use them even against poorer targets.

One report filed with the Army reached the conclusion that to be effective in battle tactical atomic weapons might have to be used by the thousands. At first glance this estimate might seem excessively high for it would mean that atomic destruction would completely embrace a battle area hundreds of miles long and tens of miles deep. An additional fact might seem to make the estimate seem much too high: in the strategic air war against Germany the Allies dropped upon the cities the equivalent of one hundred A-bombs. As many American tourists know from first-hand experience the devastation visited upon German cities was appalling. The error in the comparison is that cities with their fixed structures and definite locations on the geographic map are quite unlike battlefields. It is more to the point to compare the number of heavy artillery shells fired by the U.S. Ground Forces in the last war and to try to estimate how many A-bombs would be required to produce the same damage. Our Armed Forces used up a veritable mountain of munitions adding up to about 4 million tons. In this total were included some 30 million rounds of heavy artillery shells. A rough estimate shows that it would take about 8,000 A-shells to equal the fire power packed in this steel and high explosive barrage. Add to this, tactical bombing supplied by the Allied Air Force, and the number of A-bombs goes even higher. Therefore, it may well be that the estimate of thousands of A-bombs for the battlefield is not too excessive.

As a sequel to the question of "how many bombs" one may naturally ask, "Do we have enough atomic material to make enough A-bombs?" Apparently the answer must be in the negative for, as we have noted in Chapter 4, one expansion of atomic facilities followed another, the most recent being a $3 billion appropriation authorized by the Congress in the 1953 budget. The late Senator McMahon has furnished the rationale of this series of expansions as follows:

Five years ago neither the professional soldiers nor the atomic scientists foresaw what will turn out to be the great military revolution—the use of atomic energy as fire power in the hands of troops, sailors, and airmen. It was this revolution that brought about the requirement for great numbers of atomic bombs.

In justification of the large expansion programs one may point out that atomic energy represents a new field of man's endeavor and it would be shortsighted to base all one's estimates upon expected developments. In the atomic field the unexpected should be expected. For example, there may be a startling development in, say, harnessing atomic power for propelling aircraft. If such were the case then previous estimates of how much nuclear fuel would be required would undoubtedly have been too conservative. On the other hand there has been considerable wild-blue-yonder speculation on the uses of atomic energy. Some of the applications such as the use of A-weapons in antiaircraft shells need to be taken with great reserve. If such a development were technically possible it is by no means clear that atomic ack-ack would satisfy a pressing military requirement. Nor does the need for an atomic warhead for a torpedo seem to present an immediate need for great amounts of fissionable material. The real targets for atomic torpedoes would be the enemy's submarine pens for the Soviets have no Navy to shoot at. Soviet submarines could be put out of action by a homing torpedo armed with T.N.T. just as effectively as one carrying an atomic war head.

It will not be very long before the total national investment in atomic energy since its development will total $10 billion. This is certainly a formidable amount of money for any weapon development yet the late Senator McMahon has called the A-bomb "our best and cheapest" weapon. Estimates of the cost of a single A-bomb vary all over the lot and matters are not helped by the development of different power bombs each of which requires a somewhat different amount of nuclear explosive—the determining factor in the weapon cost. Clearly, the unit cost for a nominal A-bomb is well over $1 million, otherwise a total stockpile of over 10,000 bombs would be indicated and no public estimates go that high. Professor John R. Dunning of Columbia University, a leading atomic expert, has prophesied that bomb production of such a staggering stockpile might be feasible. The vast expansion in atomic production facilities certainly means that a stockpile of 10,000 A-bombs is an objective attainable before 1960.

Impressive as the total expenditures for atomic energy may be they are dwarfed by the over $200 billion spent on conventional military armaments since the war. Dollar for dollar atomic explosives are much cheaper in achieving destruction than ordinary high explosive bombs dropped by aircraft or shells fired from cannon. This is true even if one considers in his arithmetic the cost of delivering atomic weapons, for the problem of delivering a single package of a few tons of one bomb is much simpler than that of transporting thousands of one-ton packages of explosives to a target. It is, in fact, the delivery cost of a weapon that becomes such a burden to the national economy. Over-all appropriations for a year for the Strategic Air Command, which is designed to deliver atomic weapons, exceed atomic appropriations for a decade. Furthermore, expenditures on military equipment of the conventional type come under the heading of rent rather than of a capital investment. Planes obsolesce quickly and have to be replaced with more complex and more expensive items of military hardware. On the other hand A-bombs have as their critical and most expensive ingredient U-235 or Pu-239 which serves equally as well in peacetime as atomic fuel as in wartime for military explosive application. So the ton quantities of pure fissionable material which are being accumulated in deep vaults are "money in the bank."

The American taxpayer will be glad to learn that dollars spent on atomic production are redeemable with slight markdown in peacetime. However, true peacetime conditions are seemingly far away and the taxpayer is more concerned with the crushing onus of current military expenditures. He is, therefore, anxious to know whether or not the atom will aid in cutting the cost of conventional arms. This is equivalent to asking if atomic fire power will replace conventional fire and thus mean that fewer tanks, guns, and aircraft will be required. First of all, the atom has already effected real economies in national defense. Consider what the cost of a Strategic Air Command would be if ordinary T.N.T. and incendiary bombs had to be used instead of the thousand-fold more potent A-bombs. The costs would be many times higher than at present and it is doubtful if they could be met except under a condition of all-out war. The question of whether

A-shells and tactical A-bombs, delivered by plane or by missile, will substitute for the fire power of tanks, artillery, and tactical air is easily answered in the affirmative. However, as Senator Henry M. Jackson, a member of the Joint Congressional Atomic Energy Committee, points out: "Atomic armaments can never completely replace expensive conventional armaments, nor can they replace them all at once. But a sweeping replacement is in the cards as surely as day follows night." There is an enormous amount of inertia which has to be overcome in the military command processes before the military revolution inherent in atomic weapons comes about. Obviously, many battlefield situations will not be favorable to the use of atomic weapons. A general would be out of his mind to use an A-bomb to wipe out a single machine-gun nest, so he will continue to demand quantities of nonatomic weapons.

Probably, the biggest unknown in the matter of tactical A-bombs is the soldier, himself. Battlefield atomic weapons are in the final analysis a contest between man and the atom. The lowly infantryman has throughout the ages been exposed to every conceivable weapon that could be thrown at him. And he has still emerged as the irreplaceable factor in holding and taking ground. The next tableau in the history of war showing "soldier versus the atom" has yet to be depicted and any predictions about it are hazardous because no atomic weapons have yet been used on the field of battle. The late Judge Robert P. Patterson, while acting as Secretary of War, ventured the prediction: "Even with the atomic bomb and the vast panoply of ingenious weapons we have now or will have, the soldier of the Infantry will still be the backbone of the Army, the man who takes and holds the ground."

8

PEACETIME POWER

ROBERT M. HUTCHINS, then chancellor of the University of Chicago where so much wartime atomic research had centered, made some glowing predictions about atomic power in the postwar world. "Heat will be so plentiful," he said, "that it will even be used to melt snow as it falls. . . . A very few individuals working a few hours a day at very easy tasks in the central atomic power plant will provide all the heat, light, and power required by the community and these utilities will be so cheap that their cost can hardly be reckoned."

But here it is ten years since the first chain reaction was achieved on the University of Chicago campus and the public has yet to see the practical benefits of atomic power. No central atomic power plant has yet been built nor has even a prototype plant been constructed. Just what is wrong? Even granting Mr.

Hutchins' indulgence in hyperbole, surely atomic power ought to be somewhere in the picture soon.

To understand the lack of progress in our atomic power program it is necessary to trace the developments from the 1944-45 period up to the present time. First, we should be perfectly clear about one thing. Scientists, today, know of no way to extract atomic power from uranium except through the agency of a nuclear reactor. The reactors put into operation at Hanford during 1944 were the most powerful of any built during the war but, as we have noted, none of these generated any useful power. Cooling water from the broad Columbia River was pumped through aluminum channels to take the heat away from the uranium rods and this water was then stored for a while to dissipate any radioactivity; thereupon it was poured back into the mighty Columbia, heating it up ever so slightly.

Every nuclear reactor which had been built during the war worked successfully and scientists looked forward to the postwar period when they could design reactors to produce useful power. It seemed only a small step to jump from a design which could produce plutonium to one which could produce useful power. Accordingly, physicists, chemists, and engineers buttonholed Congressmen to emphasize the great potential of this new power source. There was great fear that the heavy hand of military control would stay the proper development of atomic power and this was one of the biggest reasons why a civilian Atomic Energy Commission was proposed and finally established. But during the first year of the postwar period no atomic power plant was destined to be constructed. Nor in any of the five years to follow.

An atomic power plant might have been built and operated within this time period. Dr. Farrington Daniels, then director of what was then to become the Argonne National Laboratory, had actually drawn up plans for an experimental power plant. I was working as his assistant at the time and I remember the long hours which he devoted to the project. His enthusiasm for the work was contagious and he soon persuaded his friend Dr. Charles Thomas, now president of the Monsanto Chemical Company, to join forces in building the world's first A-power plant. I still have in my files a faded copy of the April 13, 1946, press release, given out by General L. R. Groves, announcing that the atomic pilot plant would be built at Oak Ridge and would be "ready to operate sometime late this year or early next year." Despite Dr. Daniels' dogged persistence this experimental reactor was never built. It is not easy to put one's finger on the basic reason why this first pile died a-borning. For one thing there was the hiatus between military and civilian control and the resultant confusion which this entailed. Then there was the conservatism of the newly established Atomic Energy Commission.

The early days of atomic power development were marked by indecision and by a general attitude of playing-it-safe. Such a policy was in violent contrast with the bold wartime attitude toward challenging technical problems. The end result was that no new nuclear reactors other than research types were built. Officials within the AEC, especially those at the policy-making level, were fearful that an expensive new reactor might not work or might work only for a short time so they were careful to refer all new reactor proposals to special committees for scientific study and evaluation. During this period the atomic agency spawned a record number of Washington committees which scrutinized power plant designs with a fine-toothed scientific comb. The total effect was to effectively stymie reactor development, causing the noted reactor expert, Dr. Eugene P. Wigner, to remark: "What the Commission needs most is to build a pile that will not work." This heretical observation expressed the situation all too well; the AEC badly needed to adopt a bold approach with an engineering flavor rather than continue a stalemate.

Dr. Wigner's pungent criticism of the AEC's work on A-power was made at a conference within the guarded area at Oak Ridge. It was not published, for scientists had no desire to criticize the agency for whose creation they had fought so gallantly. Criticism might have served to make legislators change their mind on the matter of civilian control of atomic energy. Senators like Mc-Kellar and Hickenlooper might have been only too glad to conduct a spectacular investigation of the new agency and return atomic energy to the generals.

Postwar optimism about the peacetime benefits of atomic energy bloomed during the 1946-47 period even as it became apparent that the prime benefit would be atomic power, and even as this development inched along in the laboratories. Atomic scientists were still very much in demand on the lecture platform and many an audience was enthralled by a speaker who spoke of "deserts blooming" under the radiance of A-power. Many a listener was overawed by the prediction that a small piece of uranium no larger than a cube of sugar could produce power equaled only by one hundred tons of coal.

There was no disputing the scientific facts about uranium power. A single pound of U-235 or Pu-239 if completely fissioned would produce heat that was equal to that produced by about 1,300 tons of coal. Pound for pound this new atomic fuel releases 2,600,000 times more energy than coal. But this does not mean that this energy is easily available or can be obtained from small pellets of uranium. An analogy may be of some help in understanding this situation. Having pure uranium is like having gasoline so far as its explosiveness is concerned. It is relatively easy to explode a gallon of gasoline; merely allow it to evaporate in a room, set off a spark, and an explosion will result. It is somewhat harder to make the U-235 explode in a bomb but it can be done easier than it can be made to produce useful power. To generate power, as in the case of gasoline, one needs a machine to harness the energy. The internal combustion engine was the invention which made possible the use of gasoline for producing controlled power. The nuclear chain reactor is the machine which harnesses the power of the atom, and like the gasoline engine it is a complex machine.

Development of atomic power machines has been hindered by two obstacles which did not interfere in the case of the evolution of the gasoline engine. One is the stultifying secrecy which screens off A-power work from the public view and thus from the helpful criticism which results from public assessment of any project. The deleterious effects of such secrecy are considered in detail in Chapter 11. The other barrier to atomic progress is the airtight monopoly which the Atomic Energy Commission exercises over the direction of all atomic activities. Such a monopoly thwarts the spirit of free enterprise and individual initiative which are so fundamental to the American way of life.

Recognizing the need for greater industrial participation in its program the Atomic Energy Commission wisely called in a group of prominent industrialists and asked them to advise as to the means by which American industry might assume a larger role in atomic energy development. These businessmen formed the Industrial Advisory Group which submitted its recommendations to the AEC in December of 1948. This report stressed the need for greater industrial participation and observed:

The difficulty and the danger in the present situation is that industry's part in atomic energy is very limited as compared with opportunities which exist and always have existed in other fields. The small number of companies which take significant part are selected by the Government and the extent of their role in the work is limited by specific assignments from the Government.

It continued:

It has been stated that industrial opportunities in atomic energy are potentially unlimited. But they are at present so shadowy that business men neither know where to look nor what to look for. Today no one can say whether the prospect of profits or other incentives exist, because under present conditions the great majority in industry know little or nothing about the subject.

The Industrial Advisory Group prescribed some stiff medicine for the AEC in making constructive suggestions for improving industry's part in atomic developments. It took the AEC to task for having a poor administrative organization and it urged an organizational shake-up. Actually, the exploratory work of the Advisory Group led to extensive reorganization even before the final report was published. One of the most constructive recommendations made in the report was that the AEC should establish a new Division of Reactor Development to have full responsibility for the reactor program.

During the time that the industrialists were busy looking into what was wrong with the Commission's reactor work it became clear to almost everyone who had access to the program that atomic power was not going to see the light of day very soon. In the fall of 1948 David Lilienthal stated that "the first commercially practical atomic power plant is not just around the corner, nor around two corners." He further predicted that it would be from eight to ten years before the technical obstacles would be hurdled and a practical power plant would be demonstrated to run on uranium fuel. A few months later the General Advisory Committee, whose members were appointed by the President to act as guides to the AEC, submitted a report which concluded: "We do not see how it would be possible under the most favorable circumstances to have any considerable portion of the present power supply of the world replaced by nuclear fuel before the expiration of 20 years."

Thus the pendulum of opinion swung from a high point of optimism and arced downward. The gloom of pessimism hung over atomic power development. The explanation for this rather rapid turn-around on the prospects for A-power can only be partially found in the tough technology of the reactor field. There is no doubt that everyone had taken too rosy a view of atomic power and had discounted the tasks which had to be accomplished before atomic power would be a reality. But basically, the approach to making new reactors was highly conservative and overly scientific. As one of the few nuclear engineers in the country once remarked to me: "The scientists are in the driver's seat and they are trying to make the first pile too perfect." Furthermore, there was no inspiring goal to postwar atomic work to key up morale on the project. So the decline of optimism about A-power can be chalked up to more than one factor.

The first statement of a concrete reactor program was given by Dr. Robert F. Bacher, a member of the Commission, in a speech delivered February 9, 1949. Dr. Bacher announced that the AEC would proceed to build four new reactors and that these would form the backbone of the nation's reactor development program. At about this same time there was established the Division of Reactor Development to implement the new reactor program. Dr. L. R. Hafstad was selected to be director of the new division. Thus the basis was laid for a concerted attack upon the problem of making uranium yield its contained power to the will of man.

Of the four reactors slated for construction two were designed to be prototypes of naval propulsion units. These will be discussed in the next chapter. The other two included a *materials testing reactor* or MTR as it is known today which was designed to provide an intensely hot atomic oven for testing how the various reactor materials would endure the conditions inside a nuclear reactor. The *experimental breeder reactor* or EBR was the other nuclear machine and its purpose was stated as being the critical testing of whether a nuclear reactor could "breed" fissionable material. By "breeding" one means producing more fissionable material, say, Pu-239, than is consumed in the operation of the reactor. Breeding is of such importance that it will be discussed in greater detail later in this chapter.

The simultaneous creation of the Reactor Development Division and the announcement of a firm program of reactor construction marked a turning point in the atomic power doldrums. In part, this new activity was the result of the criticism of the Industrial Advisory Group and in part it derived from pressure applied by the Navy Department to speed up work on an atomic engine for submarine propulsion. Looked at in retrospect, this military pressure to develop atomic engines thereafter became a dominant factor in the AEC's reactor program. I may be expressing a minority opinion but from personal observations of how the AEC viewed reactor development, I feel that its emphasis of the naval reactor in its atomic program was more than required to fulfill the military requirement. I feel that when the atomic agency discovered that a single nuclear reactor would cost between $25 and $50 million it became weak-kneed about asking Congress for such appropriations for nonmilitary reactors. There was also the bugaboo that one of these reactors might fail to function properly and if this happened the resulting Congressional investigation would jeopardize all atomic power development. I believe that these factors were instrumental in causing the AEC to shift the emphasis in its program from civilian A-power to military atomic propulsion. At the risk of being labeled an idealist I feel that atomic power development should have been deemed important enough to stand upon its own two feet and not be brought in, limping on a military crutch.

My personal belief, and I label it as such, is that the AEC's decision to make its reactor program conform to a military posture was dictated more by political convenience than by the desire to meet a military requirement. At the time that the switchover occurred in the power program I was working for the Research and Development Board in the Pentagon and I took pains to explore the military priority for an atomic submarine. I discovered that the Joint Chiefs of Staff had assigned a priority to the nuclear propulsion of undersea craft but upon further inquiry this turned out to be a desirable military objective rather than an urgent military necessity. The Navy Department, at the time, was not sold upon the atomic submarine and its enthusiasm for the project was largely centered upon a single naval officer, Captain H. G. Rickover. More than any one person, civilian or military, Captain Rickover was responsible for getting the Navy interested in A-power and his adventures in this new field will be described in the following chapter.

Some officials within the AEC have claimed that the military route to A-power is actually the shortest road to civilian atomic power utilization. They point out that history records many cases where a technical development was greatly aided by the urgency of the military application, the lightweight Diesel engine and jet aircraft being cases in point. On this line of reasoning it is held that the age of atomic power will come sooner because of the acceleration caused by intensive military development of atomic engines. There is some truth in this assertion but considering the technical developments it seems that making an atomic engine for a submarine before a land-based civilian power plant is putting the cart before the horse. It is much more difficult to design and construct a reactor which has to be squeezed into the confines of a submarine hull, which has to be absolutely leakproof regarding radioactive contamination, and which has to have the flexibility and ruggedness to stand up under the rigors of undersea operation. At any rate our atomic program is patterned to a military profile and civilian power seems destined to be a by-product of the U.S. Navy.

So for better or for worse the reactor program in this country was started anew in the first days of 1949 as a two-pronged attack upon atomic power. One prong consisted of the two experimental reactors just mentioned, and the other was composed of two larger and more costly naval reactors to be built by the General Electric Company and the Westinghouse Electrical and Manufacturing Corporation.

Both the experimental reactors, the one for testing materials and the other for breeding, were constructed at a 400,000-acre Nuclear Reactor Testing Station which consisted in part of the former Naval Proving Ground located near Arco, Idaho. The remoteness of this site was deemed to be a desirable feature since relatively large amounts of radiation would be produced by the reactors and health authorities wished to minimize the danger of radioactivity to any nearby city.

All details of these two nuclear reactors were kept highly secret. No one outside the barbed-wire fences was permitted to examine the AEC's reactor program and therefore effective criticism of the work in progress was barred. Criticism could, therefore, come only from persons who knew what was going on inside the secret areas. Now this means that there could be only three sources of criticism. One source could be someone in the Atomic Energy Commission who indulged in self-criticism. No such criticism is on record for it runs contrary to the fundamental rules of a government agency to criticize one's self. A second source could be people outside the AEC who became acquainted with the *status quo* of secret work on the basis of their previous experience, their appraisal of published information, and careful evaluation of what AEC personnel said in public. There is very little of such criticism, one exceptional case being a letter which Nobel prize winner Harold C. Urey wrote to the editor of the *New York Times* on May 11, 1950. In this letter to the editor Dr. Urey inserted a barbed paragraph which we shall quote in full:

In view of the effective competition in atomic energy development which we now have [note: the reference here is to Soviet work], a much more daring approach to these problems is needed. We need more self-starters in a position to make decisions, and less of the cautious administrators. In fact, we shall be making progress when we work in such ways that some things attempted do not behave as expected, that is, when some reactor explodes or does not react at all.

A veritable bombshell of criticism came from a third source, namely, from a former employee of the Atomic Energy Commission. Dr. Kenneth S. Pitzer was director of research for the AEC and after resigning he made a speech on March 7, 1952, which echoes Dr. Urey's words, the difference being that the echoes were much stronger. Pulling no punches, Dr. Pitzer deplored the slowness of the development in power reactor designs and attributed this to "an unwillingness of the Commission to proceed with any of these designs until all of its advisers agreed that this was the best design."

As director of the AEC's research program, Dr. Pitzer had access to almost everything within the Commission. Therefore, his critical remarks deserve the closest scrutiny and merit respect. They constitute practically the only appraisal of atomic power by an ex-AEC official and the fact that they are of a critical nature and imply a lack of progress in atomic power should be of great importance to everyone interested in the new field. One thing which Dr. Pitzer decried was the rule by committee (there were sixteen committees at last count) within the Commission and in his own words: "There are now too many cooks tasting the broth before it is served; there are now too many sources of high level negative decision which, once rendered, is then nearly impossible to overcome." One of the committees which Dr. Pitzer had in mind was one which recommended that no experimental reactors be built near big cities, where the AEC main laboratories were located, but that they be constructed at a remote location. This decision led to the establishment of the Arco Test Station and in Dr. Pitzer's opinion "this decision delayed the reactor development program at least a year." He also pointed out that "some of these Committee members of long standing seem to have remarkably little enthusiasm for the primary goals of the Atomic Energy Program," and he recommended that their jobs should be given to "men of comparable stature who are on record as believing great new developments in atomic energy are possible."

The basic reason why the atomic power program has been hidden from public view is that authorities claim that this is essential for national security. They point out that a nuclear reactor of improved design is a better producer of fissionable material and by revealing design details or even its rated power to the Russians we would be helping them. However, the basic premise in this argument is that the United States is guarding secrets about superior nuclear reactors. If the result of secrecy is to condone a laggardly development of nuclear reactors and to keep in existence mediocre designs of these machines then there is no sense in this policy. All we are doing then is fooling ourselves and hurting our own progress while the Soviets forge ahead of us in their own reactor designs. We must not forget the unalterable fact that six years elapsed in the postwar period before a power reactor was operated and this only on a pilot-scale basis.

One of the most deplorable aspects of any monopoly is that those who control it may dictate its policies without regard to the best interests of the public. Adding the element of secrecy to a monopoly makes the situation almost vicious for then the public can not look closely at the monopoly and see what is going on and if it is in the public interest. Mr. Lilienthal pointed his finger at the official monopoly on atomic power in an article in *Collier's* with a persuasive appeal to free the atom. He argued that "The time for the first industrial applications of atomic knowledge is overdue—let's end government monopoly and give American competitive industry a chance."

Dr. Charles A. Thomas, president of the Monsanto Chemical Company, publicly proposed that industry be invited by the government to help develop atomic power on its own initiative. He offered a plan for such co-operation and described it as one which "contemplates the design, construction, and operation of atomic power plants built by industry with its own funds, producing power and plutonium in the same plant. . . . The uranium, the necessary source of power, could be loaned or leased by the Government to the industrial plant, which could convert a portion of it into plutonium and power. The power would belong to the industry that put up the money but the plutonium . . . would belong to the Government." By this process Dr. Thomas hoped that private enterprise impelled by the profit motive would be able to produce fissionable material for the government at a lower price than now obtained. The Thomas proposal is a daring one but is in the best American tradition; it is to be hoped that it will be acted upon favorably by the Atomic Energy Commission.

From what limited criticism has been voiced of the U.S. atomic power program it would seem that things are not moving as fast as they could. Is the country to persist in this stationary state or will the logjam in the A-power situation be smashed? The indications are hopeful and some optimism is warranted on the basis of events which occurred in 1952. After years of indecision and faltering activity the tempo of the AEC's reactor program noticeably quickened. Both its nonmilitary reactors, the MTR and the EBR, were finished and brought up to power.

The MTR or materials testing reactor is the most expensive of the two, costing in excess of $31 million and it is also the most powerful. Designed to provide a fiery atomic furnace for testing materials to be used in other reactors the MTR unit is a valuable tool in the reactor program. Instead of guessing how a given material will stand up under the heat and penetrating rays within the heart of a reactor scientists can now insert specimens into this experimental reactor and test their behavior directly. This testing is highly important because it is known that within the reactor core materials are constantly bombarded by penetrating rays which produce decided physical changes such as differences in thermal characteristics, in strength, and in resistance to creep. Unfortunately, many ordinary construction materials cannot be used in reactors because of their retarding effect upon the chain reaction and those which can be used do not always have the best physical and chemical characteristics. Much of reactor engineering concerns itself with the task of producing materials which will behave satisfactorily inside a reactor. For example, recent experiments show that zirconium, a metal previously a rarity, will be useful as a reactor material and efforts have been made to mass produce this element in pure form.

The EBR or experimental breeder reactor, the less powerful and less expensive nuclear reactor, constitutes an important step forward in reactor development. It is a relatively small-size reactor of quite novel design. The core consists of a retaining vessel into which protrude jacketed rods of enriched uranium. Around these circulate a liquid metal, presumably a sodium-potassium alloy, which serves to remove the heat from the reactor core. The heated liquid metal is conducted by pipes from the core out to a heat exchanger and is then recirculated in the reactor. For demonstration purposes a small amount of heat has been taken from the heat exchanger and converted into electricity in the usual way. However, this was not the main purpose of the reactor. Its chief purpose is to demonstrate whether or not it is possible to breed plutonium, that is, to convert uranium into plutonium and do this so efficiently that more plutonium is produced in the reactor than is burned up in the fission process. Plutonium could be used in the fuel rods of the breeder reactor but it is dangerous to handle and for the first unit U-235 was selected. Thus to be correct we have to say that breeding in the EBR reactor will be achieved when more plutonium is made than U-235 is consumed.

When this book went to press breeding had not been achieved, or at least had not been announced, yet the basic facts are such that one can assume that it will be possible to breed nuclear fuel in a reactor. The trick in making a reactor that will breed is to be so stingy with the ways that neutrons are lost in the reactor that you have enough of them left over to use for converting U-238 into Pu-239. In the case where we use U-235 as the nuclear fuel for fission we know that each time an atom of U-235 is split 2.5 neutrons are released. This is an average figure since in a single fission process one might have two or three neutrons, it not being possible to chop a neutron in two by the fission process. To keep the chain reaction perking along one has to use one of these 2.5 neutrons. This leaves 1.5 neutrons left over. If breeding is just achieved then one of these 1.5 neutrons will have to be captured in U-238 to produce an atom of Pu-239 so that we have a margin of .5 neutrons which we can afford to waste in the reactor. This is a slender margin since there are a number of ways in which neutrons can be taken away from the chain reaction. They may be lost simply by wandering out of the pile, or they may be captured in U-235 without causing fission, or they may be gobbled up by neutron-hungry elements in the reactor. Boron, for example, has a large appetite for neutrons and one has to be careful that reactor materials do not contain even traces of this element.

Men who are close to the reactor development program feel that breeding will be possible but if the EBR unit does not breed there is a little-known fact which evokes optimism. It involves a little nuclear arithmetic but only a very little. While U-235 emits 2.5 neutrons per fission it is known that Pu-239 emits more neutrons than this, actually, about three neutrons per fission. Thus if one substitutes plutonium for the enriched uranium fuel rods in the EBR unit it should be possible to have breeding. Although no details of the reactor core have been published it is probable that the physical arrangement for breeding will be in the nature of a natural uranium blanket surrounding the reactor core. Thus the neutrons emerging from the core will strike the uranium, which is 99.3 per cent U-238, and convert it to plutonium. This artificially manufactured element can then be chemically separated from the uranium. Since the plutonium produced rivals the U-235 consumed as nuclear fuel and since the fission reaction produces heat which can be used as power the breeder reactor in effect makes it possible to have your cake and eat it, too. One can burn up a pound of U-235, produce heat equal to 1,300 tons of coal, and at the same time produce a pound of plutonium or slightly more than a pound, depending upon how well the reactor is designed. In terms of a conventional coal-fired power plant this would be like shoveling in coal on one side of the plant, producing the desired power, and at the same time taking out on the other side more coal than you burned.

The great significance of breeding is that it allows man to tap all of the fission energy in natural uranium. Without breeding man would be essentially restricted to using only the U-235 content of uranium and this as we have seen is only .7 per cent of natural uranium. In theory, at least, breeding makes the 140-fold more abundant U-238 convertible to a fissionable material and thus expands enormously the energy reserves available in uranium ores. It also means that one can make use of the thorium ores which are fairly abundant in nature. The latter is possible because thorium, like U-238, is what we call a fertile material; it can be converted into a fissionable material. Neutrons impinging upon thorium can cause it to transform to a new isotope of uranium, called U-233. Uranium-233 like U-235 and Pu-239 is a fissionable material; these are the only fissionable materials now of practical importance. Of the "big three" only U-235 is found in nature and for this reason our whole atomic energy program depends upon U-235 and thus upon uranium ore. Uranium is, therefore, the keystone of atomic energy.

We have mentioned that the experimental breeder plant produced token amounts of electricity for demonstration purposes. A whole series of questions must immediately jump to the forefront of the reader's mind. At the risk of being thought proleptic the writer lists just a few: How soon will A-power be practical? How much will the new power cost? Will it effect drastic cuts in the monthly electric bill? Unfortunately, there are no firm answers to these questions and at best one can hazard only estimates. To a large extent the speed with which atomic power comes into its own depends upon how much the American people demand it. The Atomic Energy Commission nor any other government agency does not have a rigid timetable for atomic power development. In fact, civilian atomic power is currently being by-passed in favor of military A-power. As the chairman of the AEC, Gordon Dean, stated: "We are going after the submarine reactor first. But in doing so, we are at least building a reactor that will produce useful power, and the dividend in knowledge that we gain will have a direct and immediate application to our effort to produce commercial civilian power. As a matter of fact, it is probably very fortunate from the peacetime point of view that the Navy wants an atomic-powered submarine for this gives us the incentive of working on a reactor for a real, practical purpose at a time when otherwise we would probably have to stick to research and development machines."

At the present stage of the atomic power game it is not possible to predict whether this new power source will be able to compete with power produced by what we know as fossil fuels—coal, oil, and natural gas. No practical atomic power plants for generating, say, 100,000 kilowatts of electricity have been produced. To judge from the most recent data which have been released it would appear that such a power plant is still more than several years in the future. The fact that atomic power may have a high initial cost should not deter plant construction nor curb enthusiasm for the power source. No one should expect that the first A-power plant would compete with a coal-fired plant. Very few major developments achieve their final perfection at the first hatching. We should be willing to subsidize the first dozen A-power plants in order to iron out the bugs in the designs and learn how future costs can be cut.

A special committee formed from representatives of the electric power industry was established by the AEC to report on industrial interest in atomic power and in its initial report issued on June 20, 1951, it summed up the dollars-and-cents aspect of atomic energy with the conclusion:

It is clear to us that no valid judgment can yet be made as to whether and on what scale nuclear reactors will ultimately contribute to our energy resources. . . . No one should expect that commercially feasible atomic power would mean radical reductions in power costs. There is little if any prospect that the over-all cost reduction could be revolutionary.

The reason why your electric bill will not be cut in half by atomic power is that the capital costs for an A-power plant may be higher than for a coal-steam plant. Even if the reactor were a power-breeder and you got your fuel for nothing you would still have the very significant operating, maintenance, and fixed costs. In addition the cost of chemical processing of the used and new atomic fuel would be considerable. To top this off one has to add the cost of transmitting the electricity to your home through a complex power grid so that even if you got your fuel at no cost this would probably slice off no more than 25 per cent from your monthly electric bill. People who live in regions where electricity is produced by hydroelectric power stations, where the fuel costs are zero, know that they still have to pay sizeable electric bills.

While atomic power may not affect the consumer's pocketbook very much and certainly not very soon, it may be of greater and more immediate importance to certain American industries. For example, there are industrial operations which use huge amounts of electric power in reducing aluminum and magnesium, in producing chlorine, and in the electrolytic refining of copper. Such plants might be preferred consumers of electricity produced by A-power for they represent a constant demand for power and use short simple feeder lines in contrast to the fluctuating civilian demand for electricity which must be distributed through a complex and costly transmission network. Moreover, there are special industries such as those involved in primary treatment of ores which would profit greatly if a large source of electricity could be moved close to the minehead. Mining operations often take place in remote locations far from cheap power, and bulky ore has to be transported to processing plants which have abundant sources of power. An example is found in the phosphate industry where exploitation of western deposits is prevented because of absence of nearby electric power to heat the electric furnaces. Hydroelectric power is not always available and coal is expensive to transport to inaccessible regions so that uranium as an essentially weightless fuel holds promise for industries which could operate most efficiently at the minehead. Such industries might be able to pay a premium for atomic power and if no premium were required they might blossom forth in profusion. Small cities might spring up in mountain or isolated areas where previously only a small settlement existed to claw ores from the earth.

Prospects for power reactors are much better if industrial processes can use the heat produced directly without going to the trouble of converting it to electricity. Theoretically, only the practical problem of finding reactor materials to withstand high temperatures limits the degree of heat producible in the nuclear reactor. From a strictly scientific viewpoint the initial temperature of fission corresponds to about 500 million degrees centigrade; this has to be stepped down to less than 2,000°C to be of practical use to man. This is quite a comedown for the atom and one wonders whether it may not be possible to devise ways to utilize the extremely high temperatures available from the atom. High temperature reactions might make possible a whole new chemical-metallurgical industry, but this must be labeled as speculation for man still has to restrict himself to a few thousand degrees of temperature because the atomic furnace must have a wall.

This is probably a good place to point out that one good customer for atomic power would be the Atomic Energy Commission, itself. As of mid-1953 its plants are estimated to use about 2½ per cent of the total installed power capacity of the United States. Yet as of the same date the useful power produced by the nuclear reactors of the atomic project would not provide enough electricity to light the street lamps of a small village.

When we talk of atomic power we must look to the future not only because A-power is still in the embryo state but because our energy resources are not unlimited and we must look around for new sources to drive our ships, light our houses, and keep the wheels of industry turning. We must remember that the U.S.A. is a power-hungry country with a keen appetite for kilowatts. Ever since electricity came of age the U.S. electric utilities have roughly doubled their generating capacity every ten years. By

1954 it is probable that the installed electrical generating capacity in this country will exceed 100 million kilowatts. The electric power and light industry is currently spending more than $2 billion annually in a major expansion program which is scheduled to add a yearly average of about 10 million kilowatt capacity to the U.S. generating capacity. The bulk of our electricity is produced in coal-fired plants and each year well over 100 million tons of coal are burned in power plant furnaces. If all of these plants ran on atomic power rather than on coal they would burn up in excess of 40 tons of pure U-235 or Pu-239 or roughly 6,000 tons of natural uranium per year.

The coal we burn to produce electricity is only a fraction of the total mined each year, for the majority is used for other purposes such as in industry, transportation, commerce, and in home heating. Thus when we consider the role of atomic energy as a power source we should not confine our attention solely to the production of electricity. Looking at the total consumption of energy resources in the United States two things are outstanding. First, the rate at which we are depleting our energy resources is increasing and, second, the rate at which the so-called premium fuels are being consumed is increasing rapidly. The latter point needs no statistics for substantiation for everyone knows how Diesel-electric engines have replaced the old steam locomotives, how the motor car has skyrocketed the consumption of gasoline, and how home heating has boosted the sales of natural gas.

If an atomic industry is to prosper it is absolutely imperative that it be a competitive one in which American ingenuity and the incentive of profit can take effect. Had the development and production of automobiles been entrusted to the Department of Commerce rather than to private industry there would not be the 52 million vehicles which are on the road today. The production lines in Detroit and elsewhere around the nation turn out over 5 million cars a year. Such a production bonanza would be unthinkable under a government monopoly. The mushroom growth of the radio and television industry rivals that of the automotive field and again points to the desirability and essentiality of private enterprise as the best American way of doing business.

9

ATOMIC ENGINES

So MANY fables have been told about the miraculous feats which atomic power will perform in driving ships, planes, and rockets that one may easily be led to the conclusion that Buck Rogers and his interplanetary space ships are but a stone's throw away. Even without journeying into space the rumors about atomic energy have persuaded many that it will not be long before gasoline filling stations will be obsolete; all one will have to do is to flip a uranium pellet in the gas tank and drive around the world.

A pellet of pure U-235 the size of a small marble has enough energy in it to drive a modern automobile 100,000 miles or four times around the earth. But no scientists have yet discovered any way of getting any power from just one ounce of uranium. A single ounce of silvery-white U-235 has locked up in it the heat of 30,000 gallons of gasoline but the motor for generating atomic power, unlike a gasoline engine which can run with only a cupful of gasoline in the tank, requires a full charge of uranium before it will operate at all. An atomic engine has the peculiarity that it will not start unless its "gas tank" is full to the brim. Furthermore, the atomic engine must have a full supply of its uranium fuel or it will not continue to operate once started.

In the internal combustion engine, such as a gasoline-powered automobile, power is produced by the expansion of hot gases in the piston chamber. These hot gases produced by the ignition of a gasoline-air mixture push against the piston forcing it down and thus turning the drive shaft of the engine. This power is then transmitted to the rear wheels of the car by means of gears. Comparing this power conversion with the atomic engine we note that the power produced is also heat but it cannot be used as in an internal combustion engine. The heat must be removed from the core of the nuclear reactor by means of some coolant which circulates through it; this liquid is heated and may then be passed through what is called a heat exchanger. In the latter steam can be produced and this can be used to drive a turbine which in turn may generate electricity. From this brief description it should be evident that much of atomic power engineering is conventional in scope and pertains to heat exchangers, pumps, turbines, and generators. The core of the nuclear reactor serves as an intense source of heat and this heat once produced must be handled in much the same way as in a coal-fired boiler.

Atomic engines, however, have some important differences as compared with conventional engines. In the first place, the matter of controlling the nuclear reactor and changing its power is not achieved as in a gasoline engine by opening up the carburetor and feeding more gas into the engine. Instead, the heat generated in the reactor core is controlled by moving control rods in and out of the structure. The rods are specially coated so that elements in them act as a wet blanket for the chain reaction, that is, they absorb neutrons in the reactor and determine the rate at which the chain reaction proceeds. Withdrawing a control rod from the reactor increases the power for there is less of the rod inside the pile and consequently fewer neutrons are robbed from the chain reaction. Pushing the control rod back into the machine serves to decrease the power and when all the way in the control rod completely stops the chain reaction.

Controls for atomic engines have to be made foolproof so that there is no chance for the chain reaction to "run away" and lead to a disaster. The design must be such that there are safety precautions built into the reactor which will prevent the machine from getting out of control. Were the chain reaction to get out of hand the power in the machine would increase quickly, much faster than heat could be taken from the machine, and the materials inside the reactor would melt and the whole engine would be ruined. No atomic bomb explosion would result but the contents of the reactor core might be melted and spewed out, thus constituting a severe radioactive hazard. Proper design of reactors and installation of adequate controls should make atomic power plants as reliable as any modern steam power plant and there should be no trouble about locating them in metropolitan areas.

Probably the biggest problem which nuclear engineers face in designing atomic engines is the radioactive hazard. Once a nuclear reactor is assembled and started up its core becomes intensely radioactive due to the accumulation of split atoms within the uranium fuel. These fissioned atoms or fission products are very radioactive and some of them persist in emitting penetrating radiation for months and even years. This means that once a nuclear reactor goes into operation and some component within the core fails you can't shut down the plant and send in repair men to replace the defective part. As far as possible all machinery within the core of the machine must be made to function without failure or in the event of trouble means must be provided to replace the part without the human hand touching it. The latter calls for great ingenuity and for what amounts to Rube Goldberg gadgetry.

If you visit the coal-fired steam plant which supplies your electricity you can see the heart of the plant right before your eyes and see coal fed into the flames. If, someday, you are allowed to visit an Atomic Energy Commission site and see a nuclear reactor you will note a very big difference between the two kinds of power plants. The heart of the atomic power plant always has to be kept covered up with a thick shield to protect personnel from the penetrating rays emitted by the materials within the reactor core. Very often this shield consists of seven feet of solid concrete, and it envelops the reactor on all sides. Not only does the heart of the nuclear power plant have to be so shielded but anything which passes through the core, such as the coolant, has to be similarly protected. This means that the circulating pumps and the heat exchanger must also be shielded. It is this massive shield which makes an atomic engine for an automobile out of the question for it would probably run the weight of the atomic motor up to forty tons.

On your visit to your city's steam plant you would notice that the ashes from the burned coal have to be removed and you might wonder if there are any atomic ashes in the case of an atomic engine. The ashes from the fission of uranium are the two atoms into which the single uranium atom splits. We have already noted that they are a great nuisance because of their great radioactivity which persists for a long time so that even if the power plant is shut down the radioactivity lingers. In fact, these radioactive ashes also produce some heat and make it impossible to completely shut down a power plant very quickly. Like coal ash, the atomic ash must be periodically removed for it constitutes a kind of poison for the chain reaction. Some of the split atoms have a tremendous appetite for neutrons and if left in the reactor very long they would reduce the power output of the machine. To remove atomic ashes from a reactor is much more difficult and costly than shaking some grates and carting off a bucket of clinkers. The split atoms stay right in the fuel rod with the original uranium so that the whole fuel rod must be discharged from the reactor and new ones inserted.

The discharged fuel from an atomic power plant cannot be thrown away because it contains a large proportion of valuable fissionable material. It would be ideal if the fuel could be kept cooking in the reactor until all of the U-235 or plutonium were used up but long before this happens the rod deteriorates under the ceaseless bombardment of nuclear particles inside the reactor. Therefore, the discharged fuel has to be chemically processed to remove the objectionable atomic ashes or poisons and to produce pure fissionable material for use in the reactor. Such chemical processing is time-consuming and costly for it involves intensely radioactive material which must be handled with the utmost caution.

There is a vexing problem presented to health authorities in dealing with the atomic ashes and waste radioactive chemical solutions from an atomic power plant and its chemical processing plant. These cannot be dumped into a river or buried in the earth. Were the radioactive wastes emptied into a river they would prove a source of danger to fish and to any human beings who drew their water from the river. Burying the wastes in the earth, even at an isolated spot, runs the risk that they might contaminate the ground water. It must be remembered that for every pound of uranium fissioned there will be almost a pound of fission products produced and if atomic power comes into widespread use the amount of radioactivity will be prodigious. The first step in solving the problem is to concentrate the radioactive solutions so that one has to deal with a small amount of material. Then this can be encased in leakproof containers which can either be buried at sea or buried in a suitable remote area designated as an official radioactive burial grounds.

The foregoing should suffice to indicate some of the aspects of producing atomic power in a nuclear engine and to point out the unique problems associated with the latter. We are by now equipped with sufficient technical facts about atomic engines to proceed to discuss the propulsion unit which the Atomic Energy Commission and the Navy Department are collaborating on and which promises to be the world's first mobile A-power plant.

In tracing back through the records I find that the first clear-cut recognition of the possibility of using A-power in submarines is contained in a report to President Roosevelt. Dated November 1, 1939, this report states: "If the chain reaction could be controlled so as to proceed gradually, it might conceivably be used as a continuous source of power in submarines thus avoiding the use of large batteries for underwater power." Although this is the first published record I could find, I know from my work with the Navy that the Naval Research Laboratory had become interested in nuclear power in the spring of 1939 and had undertaken preliminary experiments in the field. Thereafter the Navy was almost completely frozen out of the atomic project so that there was nothing done and no interest was manifest in atomic propulsion until the end of the war.

One might have expected that after V-J Day the Navy would

have moved into the atomic power field for it is probably the world's largest consumer of premium fuels. Furthermore, it has constantly searched for new methods of propelling undersea craft, looking for fuels which would not consume precious oxygen. Moreover, the Navy is mindful of the need to do away with the dead weight of fuel storage which is such a limiting factor in marine design. And, of course, it is always on the lookout for new engines to drive ships through the seas at a faster clip. Despite all of these facts, the Navy in 1945 and for at least three years to follow seemed blind to the potentialities of atomic power.

There was one man in the Navy who did see the use for A-power. This was a slightly built but hard-bitten officer named Captain Hyman G. Rickover. Not only did he see his final objective clearly but he proceeded resolutely toward getting A-power for submarines, possessed of all the zeal and energy of a religious convert. I remember first running across Captain Rickover just after the end of the war when he visited our Chicago laboratory. At that time I had not come into contact with many naval officers but I realized immediately that Rickover was something of a phenomenon. He did not hesitate to speak his mind or to criticize anything—the latter characteristic was scarcely one which later endeared him to the Atomic Energy Commission.

Captain Rickover realized that the postwar era found the Navy in a very confused state of mind and that there was no interest in atomic propulsion. So very adroitly he did not immediately attempt to sell the big brass on this new venture; rather he gathered around himself a group of young lieutenants and proceeded to make them sweat it out at Oak Ridge, learning all the wrinkles in this new technology. There were two things which he knew were needed to pry open the door for the Navy, one was technical knowledge about atomic energy and the other was personal acquaintance with atomic scientists. It is not fair to say that Rickover and his cohorts infiltrated into the atomic energy project for this implies both stealth and a kid-gloves approach; it is more appropriate to say that the Navy secured a beachhead in the atomic field.

During the establishment of the beachhead the Atomic Energy Commission took over control of all atomic work. The perilously small naval task force clung to its position, anticipating trouble but none developed. With his landing force secure, Captain Rickover launched the second phase of his campaign. He badgered the Navy to enlist the support of the big guns in Washington, these being the admirals on Constitution Avenue. Before the naval position could be enlarged he realized that strong demands had to be made upon the AEC. In other words the Navy had to apply the pressure to the new agency in order to speed up work on naval reactors. About this time I had moved from Chicago to Washington and was working in the Pentagon as scientific adviser to the War Department and in the course of time I met Captain Rickover frequently.

One meeting I shall never forget. I dropped by Rickover's office across the street from the AEC headquarters. Greeting me with a wry smile the Captain shoved a manila folder across his desk at me. I glanced at the title on the cover "Quarterly Progress Report on Atomic Propulsion" and flipped it open. Inside there was a single blank piece of paper. "We didn't do a damned thing," he said and added some choice comments about the way in which the project was going. The latter didn't surprise me but I was intrigued with the zero-word report which Rickover had prepared for his superior, Vice-Admiral Mills, then chief of the Bureau of Ships. This was but one of the ways in which he persuaded Admiral Mills to do something about getting an atomic submarine for the Navy.

There was another meeting that is equally vivid to me. This one was a much larger and more formal affair—the annual meeting of the Symposium on Undersea Warfare, held in the auditorium of the Interior Department. There were hundreds of officers and civilians present and on the stage were Admiral Mills and an AEC commissioner, Admiral Strauss, who was presiding. Reading a prepared speech, Admiral Mills fired broadside after broadside at the Atomic Energy Commission for its failure to develop atomic power, especially for the Navy. At one point in his speech the towering Admiral turned to Admiral Strauss and interpolated: "Mind you, the Navy isn't griping but we *do* want atomic power." Admiral Strauss must have wandered back to his AEC office in a daze for he had had no advance warning of the attack.

The Navy had used its big guns for the first time and before the reverberations had ceased it was clear that the second phase of Rickover's campaign was accomplished. Any kid gloves which the Captain may have possessed were put aside in favor of a bare-knuckles approach to nuclear propulsion. Even those who held no love for Captain Rickover, and these included many officers, had to admit that he had secured his beachhead and had also succeeded in swinging top strategy around to support a major offensive.

Up to the spring of 1948 Captain Rickover had been practically the only driving force for nuclear propulsion. What he had accomplished in three years of dogged persistence he had done almost singlehanded. After Admiral Mills slam-bang speech the situation changed. The Committee on Undersea Warfare gave support to the atomic propulsion program and the Joint Chiefs of Staff officially endorsed the military objective in developing the new type submarine. Real pressure was now brought to bear upon the AEC. Lacking a real program of its own and being unable to cope with the pressure, the atomic agency formulated the reactor program which was described in the previous chapter.

These facts as I have stated them constitute to the best of my knowledge the real history of how the reactor program in the United States was shaped and how the Navy made its entry into the A-power field. Somewhere within the AEC headquarters there is probably an official history of these same developments and they probably disagree sharply with my account. Too often official histories are tidy and logical accounts of events which are neither logical nor complimentary. The facts as I have presented them are those of an eyewitness not an historian.

The events which followed the establishment of a Reactor Development Division within the AEC are largely a matter of public record. As noted in the previous chapter the Atomic Energy Commission announced early in 1949 that it would undertake construction of two nuclear reactors for producing power. At the time one of these reactors was aimed specifically at propelling a submarine and it was called STR for Submarine, Thermal Reactor. The other was designated as a different type of nuclear machine to be built by the General Electric Company to demonstrate the production of power *and* breeding in one machine. A year later, however, the reactor program underwent a shake-up and as Dr. L. R. Hafstad described this: "The planned power-breeder reactor at the Knolls Atomic Power Laboratory has been considered a casualty to the civilian cause in this readjustment." The director of the reactor program went on to say: "If military needs are such that they can help to carry the staggering financial burden of development cost, I, for one, cannot look upon these needs as a threat to the atomic power program." The power-breeder was the only one directed solely to civilian power requirements and with the readjusted AEC program it became another naval reactor known by the code letters SIR, standing for Submarine, Intermediate Reactor.

Both the STR and SIR atomic engines were to be constructed as land-based prototypes of the reactors which would thereafter be installed in submarine hulls. The Westinghouse Corporation was selected to co-operate with the Argonne National Laboratory in making the STR reactor. The Reactor Testing Station at Arco, Idaho, was designated as the site for the construction of this prototype machine. Responsibility for designing and building the SIR atomic engine was assigned to the Knolls Atomic Power Laboratory of the General Electric Company. Located near Schenectady, New York, the laboratory was also to serve as the site for the construction of the SIR prototype. Thus in the 1949-50 period the AEC and the Navy teamed up with two major American industrial organizations to design and construct two prototypes of an atomic engine for propelling a submarine.

It is expected that the STR engine will be the first to go into a hull so we shall focus attention upon it. Perhaps the reader has been puzzled by the "T" in STR; it stands for "Thermal" which means that the reactor is one in which the neutrons which cause fission are slowed down to what physicists call thermal speed. In general, there are three distinct kinds of reactors. The first is called a *fast* reactor and is so designed that the neutrons which cause fission in the machine are not slowed down once emitted in the fission process. Although we did not specify it at the time the EBR or breeder reactor is of the fast type. A second type of reactor works with neutrons which are partially slowed down and this is called an intermediate reactor. The SIR reactor is an example of this type. When the neutrons have been slowed down as much as possible they are of thermal speed and as we have just pointed out the STR reactor is of such a design. For each of these three types of reactors the design of the internal parts or the core of the machine has to be quite different.

All compact power reactors will use enriched nuclear fuel for if natural uranium were used the reactor core would have to be very large. By using uranium which has, say, 30 or 50 per cent U-235, the central part of the reactor can be made quite compact. If of cylindrical shape the diameter of the core can be from five to ten feet. The essential elements of this heart of the reactor are first a containing vessel to hold the core components; second, the fuel rods of enriched uranium; third, a suitable material such as graphite to slow down the neutrons; fourth, a coolant to remove heat from the core; and finally, control rods to operate the machine. The latter are really the only moving parts in the reactor core; they slide in and out of the core through special passages through the thick shield which envelops the core. Fission in the uranium rods is maintained at a predetermined level in the chain reaction and the fission energy converts directly to heat.

Given a powerful heat source, the conversion of this energy to useful power is an old story to industry and to the Navy. A coolant is pumped through the reactor core and carries the heat away to a heat exchanger, this also being blanketed in a thick shield to protect operating personnel from the radiation given off by the coolant. Then the heat exchanger transfers the heat to a closed cycle steam turbine which in turn is coupled to the drive shafts of the propellers.

President Truman laid the keel of the hull for the first nuclear-powered submarine on June 14, 1952. The General Dynamics Corporation of Groton, Connecticut, formerly known as the

Electric Boat Company, is constructing the submarine which is to be the first of the SSN (submarine, nuclear) type. When it is christened it will bear the illustrious name the U.S.S. *Nautilus*. Originating in Greek mythology the name was used by Jules Verne for his fictional submarine in his novel *Twenty Thousand Leagues under the Sea*. It was also the name selected by Robert Fulton for his experimental undersea craft, by Sir Hubert Wilkins for his arctic submarine, and by the Navy for a sub which accounted for almost 100,000 tons of Japanese shipping during World War II.

Navy men feel optimistic that the U.S.S. *Nautilus* will slide off the Groton ways in 1954 but some of the atomic experts are more conservative. Before the actual atomic engine for the submarine is constructed the prototype engine at the Arco test station must be put through its paces. To bridge the gap between the prototype and the actual engine the Navy has laid down requirements that the dry land model be mocked up within a section of a dummy submarine hull. At the same time it has provided an elaborate wooden dummy model of the mock-up engine to the Groton shipyards. Thus the planners hope that time can be saved in fitting the propulsion unit into the hull of the U.S.S. *Nautilus*. It is estimated that before the first atomic submarine hits the water over $60 million will have been spent on its development.

The financial bottleneck on atomic propulsion was broken shortly after the outbreak of the Korean War. A $2 billion naval construction bill was passed by the Congress and funds were included for the first atomic submarine. So far as the military services were concerned Korea took the lid off the appropriations pot. This fact undoubtedly tied in with the decision to build a second nuclear propulsion unit, that is, the SIR design.

The General Electric intermediate reactor is of more novel design than the one being built by Westinghouse and its designers feel that it will have advantages over the latter. For one thing, it is felt that the type of reactor will permit a more efficient heat transfer system. The Knolls Atomic Power Laboratory has done considerable experimenting with the use of liquid metal alloys as coolants and the combination of a smaller reactor plus a better coolant is thought to possess features of value to submarine propulsion. Atomic engines complete with their thick overcoat of shielding are by no means small engines. In fact, it required some squeezing and cutting corners on design to make the STR reactor small enough to fit in the submarine hull. Even so the U.S.S. *Nautilus* is not a sleek craft but is rather on the chubby side.

At the Knolls Atomic Power Laboratory the prototype of the SIR reactor will be built in a special housing in order to minimize any danger of radioactive contamination to the surrounding area should the unit function improperly. A huge 225-foot diameter steel sphere set on a concrete base is the structure within which the reactor will operate. After the prototype model (which may cost as much as $40 million) has been subjected to rigorous testing an engineering model will be constructed for incorporation in a second atomic submarine, the *Sea Wolf*. The hull for the latter is also being built by the General Dynamics Corporation at Groton, Connecticut. It has been announced that the atomic submarine will be of the 2,500-ton class, and it is estimated that the nuclear power plant will deliver roughly 10,000 horsepower to the propeller shafts.

Ever since 1625 when it is reported that Cornelius Drebbel, a Dutch scientist, tested a crude submarine in the Thames River, men have been looking for a true submersible. By this we mean a submarine which would have unlimited range and would not have to come up for air. Atomic propulsion fills the bill in both respects since fission does not require oxygen and since a single charge of fuel can propel a sub tens of thousands of miles. In addition atomic power promises to supply what submariners prize most highly—sustained high underwater speed. During World War II the battery-driven undersea craft could proceed at emergency speed to avoid enemy destroyers for about one and a half hours. Emergency speed was often far too slow to really get away from the enemy. Often sub skippers played possum and kept their craft motionless on the bottom to avoid detection rather than using this limited power reserve. With atomic propulsion cruising speeds of twenty-five knots should be attainable and with the speed indicator at flank (a notch above the rated "full speed") thirty knots may be reached.

Provided that the crew could endure prolonged submersion an atomic sub should be able to leave an Atlantic port, proceed to, say, Murmansk, and return without surfacing once. The advantage in staying submerged is great for this avoids radar detection. Of course, the sub would have to have its own air supply bottled up for the trip but the Navy does not seem worried about this problem. Within the submarine service officers are reluctant to make predictions about the atomic submarine. They want to have two of them, to match one against the other, to shake them down in trial runs and see just what they can do before going overboard for the new craft.

There appear to be two major uses for the faster, longer-range, atomic submarine. Members of the "silent service" within the Navy Department feel that the new submarine will be a better killer sub to track down and kill enemy submarines. The latter are the chief naval threat to the United States at the present time and for some time to come since Russia has no formidable surface fleet. Its undersea fleet, however, is formidable for it has been augmented by the latest type of German U-boats. Soviet submarines equipped to fire guided missiles at coastal cities might be a major threat to the United States, especially, if the missiles carry atomic warheads. Many officers feel that the best weapon against the threat of a submarine is another killer sub; they feel that the nuclear-powered craft will make the best killer submarine. From an offensive standpoint the Navy feels that an atomic submarine could be used to strike at critical enemy shore positions, especially at enemy submarine pens. To strike at the latter an ideal weapon would be a guided torpedo armed with an atomic warhead. Experience in the last war showed that it was virtually impossible to bomb the Nazi sub pens from above because of the mammoth concrete reinforcements used to protect them. An atomic torpedo slammed home at the submarine base could effectively put the pen out of operation. The Navy also envisages the submarine as a launching platform for guided missiles and it has already demonstrated that it is possible to launch such missiles from the deck of a sub. It may even be possible to launch an "aerial torpedo" while the submarine is below the surface.

Use of the homing underwater torpedo, armed with an A-bomb, against submarines does not seem to be indicated. If one has a good homing torpedo that is guided to the submarine then one has no need for an atomic warhead since ordinary T.N.T. warheads are quite sufficient to kill the craft. On this basis the Navy's requirement for an atomic torpedo would seem to be limited to a relatively small number of offensive applications.

Even before the first atomic propulsion engine for the U.S.S. *Nautilus* had been completed the Navy announced that it was planning to use an atomic power plant in the third of its supercarriers. Two aircraft carriers of the Forrestal class have been approved by the Congress despite bitter Air Force opposition. These ships are to be mammoth floating air bases costing about $200 million each and weighing about 60,000 tons. Normally the 1,000-foot-long supercarriers will carry about 400,000 barrels of oil as their fuel supply and this is a sizable fraction of the total weight of the ship. The battleship *Missouri*, for example, displaces 45,000 tons and carries a full fuel load of 8,800 tons of oil to power its multiple boilers the output of which is a maximum of 212,000 shaft horsepower. Although the third of the supercarriers was still not authorized the Navy went ahead with plans to install in it an atomic propulsion system. Experimental work on the huge reactor for the carrier is to be carried out at the Westinghouse Corporation's Bettis plant near Pittsburgh. No details have been made available about this power plant but it must be much more powerful, exceeding that of the U.S.S. *Missouri* and much more than the submarine power plant. The keel of the third supercarrier is not scheduled to be laid until about 1955.

When the supercarrier's atomic power plant is completed it will be similar in design to a reactor for central station power generation. No plans for any reactors of the latter type have yet been announced by the Atomic Energy Commission nor is one expected very soon but there is no technical reason why such a power reactor could not be built and operated by 1955. In connection with a high-power reactor it should be pointed out that in the long run such reactors will probably be of the breeder type since it appears unjustified, except for very high priority uses, to burn up uranium irrecoverably without attempting to generate new fissionable material in the process.

The Navy was not the only one of the military services to become involved in atomic propulsion. Shortly after the end of the war the Air Force, too, invaded the atomic energy field and it established its N.E.P.A. project—Nuclear Energy, Propulsion, Aircraft. As usual, Air Force publicists began flying atomic aircraft even before it was determined whether or not such a project were technically feasible. No wonder that the layman picking up a newspaper and reading that an atomic airplane would be flying in a year or two, became confused about nuclear-powered flight when at the same time competent scientists scoffed at these claims.

Two incidents stand out in my mind in connection with the N.E.P.A. project. The first took place early in 1947 when the project held an information meeting at Oak Ridge. I had been invited as a representative from the War Department General Staff and I was curious to see what was going on in the project. Weird rumors about the work had circulated in the Pentagon. However, nothing quite prepared me for the shock of seeing how the Air Force was approaching the problem of nuclear propulsion. There was not one competent nuclear physicist on the project although the engineers in charge trotted out big-name scientists as endorsing the project. After the meeting I returned to the Pentagon and reported that not only was money being poured down a rathole but that the Air Force was making a ludicrous approach to the problem.

The second incident was even more distressing. At the time I was working in the Research and Development Board, a high-level military agency which was supposed to watch over all research and development and advise the Secretary of Defense on the progress of weapon development. The committee to which I was attached was called upon to consider the N.E.P.A. project and despite Air Force objection it voted that "The N.E.P.A. project as it is presently constituted should be terminated promptly." This was probably the strongest language ever used by an R.D.B. committee but when it was filed with the policy board of the agency it was drastically altered. I know that the Air Force intervened and had the committee verdict changed. This, I found, was not atypical of the newly created arm of the services. Rather than admitting a mistake it preferred to bulldoze ahead and compound its errors. In this case the fundamental error had been the placing of an Air Force contract with the Fairchild Engine and Airplane Corporation, even before the scientific basis for nuclear propulsion was established.

The direct R.D.B. committee order to kill the N.E.P.A. project was not meant to kill nuclear propulsion. It was meant to put things in order so that a firm base might be laid for building up a project which might proceed toward the goal of atomic propulsion in an orderly and reasonable fashion. It should be emphasized that early in 1948 when the action was taken no thorough study had been made as to whether nuclear propulsion was feasible for aircraft. All of the technical problems which were inherently complex and hard to solve for stationary atomic power plants became much more difficult for reactors which had to generate higher power and occupy less volume. Making a reactor to propel an aircraft was not a job which the Air Force could solve by simply handing a contract to one of its aircraft manufacturers. Fundamental problems in materials, heat exchange, reactor control, and many other fields had to be licked before one could think of drawing up engineering blueprints.

All the ruckus about killing the N.E.P.A. project, although it did not cause the Fairchild contract to be canceled then, did focus attention on the problem and as a result the Atomic Energy Commission gave serious consideration to it. A special study group at the Massachusetts Institute of Technology spent a whole summer evaluating the problem and thereafter filed an analysis called the Lexington Report. While the report straddled the fence on aircraft propulsion it presented some constructive reforms to be inaugurated in the work under way and urged better co-ordination of the interested agencies in the Military Establishment, the National Advisory Committee for Aeronautics, and the Atomic Energy Commission. In essence the Lexington Report warned that atomic propulsion for aircraft would be a long and difficult goal, that much research needed to be accomplished, and that this work had better be supervised by the AEC.

In November of 1950 the AEC took over the work of the N.E.P.A. project and six months later the Air Force canceled its contract with the Fairchild Engine and Airplane Co. Nice things were said officially when the latter action took place as both the manufacturer and the Air Force tried to save face but privately scientists heaved a sigh of relief. Most of the development work on aircraft reactors was thereupon assigned to the General Electric Company's Lockland, Ohio plant.

All during the first four years of the N.E.P.A. project the Atomic Energy Commission had remarkably little to say about the possibility of making a nuclear power plant for an airplane. One can hunt through the myriad press releases, speeches, and reports but there is only oblique or vague reference made to the problem. Its one positive statement came with the announcement of the termination of the Fairchild contract and, ironically, this action was generally misinterpreted by the press. Partly due to the vagueness of the AEC and partly due to an Air Force attempt to cover up, the press came out with stories which indicated that a new phase in the aircraft reactor program had begun and that work was being accelerated. Such was not the case. What was involved was a reorientation of the aircraft propulsion program setting the sights on a longer time scale for the whole project.

No responsible AEC official has yet committed himself on the time scale for completing the first practicable aircraft reactor. Before any nuclear power plant would be used to drive an aircraft, a test-stand prototype has to be built to operate on the ground. Even then it may be necessary to go through a series of evolutions on test-stand models before a working reactor is perfected. Facilities for testing the prototype reactor are being constructed at the Reactor Testing Station in Idaho.

Once it was established that nuclear-powered flight was theoretically possible the Air Force renewed its demands to speed up work on the project by launching parallel drives to build aircraft to fit in with the atomic motors. The Air Force contracted with the Vultee Aircraft Corporation of Ft. Worth to build the air frame for the first atomic bomber. An additional contract was placed with the Pratt & Whitney Division of the United Aircraft Corporation for work on the atomic motor. Parallel development of the air frame was necessary because of the long lead time that occurs between the drawing board and the production line. In the case of the B-36 bomber this interval amounted to eight years. The fact that the air-frame design contract was awarded so recently serves as some indicator of the time when the first A-powered plane will be ready to fly.

From what we have said about nuclear reactors for submarine propulsion it should be clear that the aircraft reactor will be a fairly sizable structure. It is doubtful if the shielding for the latter reactor can be cut to less than forty tons. The weight of the reactor core would be considerably less than the shield. In contrast with the over fifty tons of fuel carried by a strategic bomber like the B-36 an atomic bomber would carry almost negligible weight of enriched uranium. Moreover, this "weightless" fuel would not have to be replenished, as a single charge of nuclear fuel would last for several round-trip missions. One of the biggest problems in making the atomic propulsion engine is that of getting power equal to more than 25,000 horsepower out of a single small reactor. For a small-size reactor the weight of the outer shield will be reduced but unfortunately the temperature inside the reactor must be much greater and this makes the design of the reactor core and its construction much more difficult.

Just when we will have nuclear-powered flight will be decided in the laboratory. If the work is prosecuted vigorously and nature is charitable the first atomic plane may be ready to take to the air within ten years. However, problems yet to be solved may delay the work by several years. I feel that it is only fair that the reader appreciate that there are still "doubting Thomases" among the scientific fraternity as to the pay-off of atomic propulsion for aircraft. One eminent scientist told me that he did not expect to see atomic planes flying in his lifetime.

Going one step further from the atomic airplane to the atomic rocket is a giant stride. There are no atomic rockets on the AEC drawing boards today. There is even considerable doubt that atomic energy will be the ultimate source of power for long-range rockets. Chemical propellents have been highly developed and while they release less energy per pound than uranium they do not require a heavy and complex engine for their use. It is foolish to say that atomic engines for rockets are an impossibility but clearly such rockets do not fall within the time span of the next ten years.

The Navy and the Air Force are the principal champions of atomic engines for propulsion and one might wonder if the Army would not find some use for atomic power. I have not found any informed Army officers who seriously propose developing atomic engines for propelling any Army vehicles such as heavy tanks. Nor does the Army seem to regard atomic energy as of much use to it except as an explosive. I once proposed that the Army would do well to develop transportable A-power stations for generating heat and power at isolated bases where other fuels are hard to obtain. Nothing ever came of the suggestion but I still feel that small A-power plants would find ready use at arctic bases.

All atomic engines are being developed in strict secrecy and as will be explained in Chapter 11 this type of development is most unfortunate. The best interests of progress and the nation's security will be satisfied if there is a minimum of secrecy enshrouding A-power development. I believe that this secrecy prevents criticism of atomic work and that the latter is the most sorely needed missing ingredient of our atomic program today.

10

THE ATOM—MAN'S SERVANT

THERE is little doubt that the principal peacetime benefit of atomic energy is the applied power which we have just discussed. Unfortunately the situation today is still such that atomic power has yet to become a practical benefit so far as the man in the street is concerned. There is a by-product of atomic power which is already of practical value to humanity and, while it is a by-product, it does not have to await the coming of the Age of A-Power to be a servant to man. This by-product is the radioactive material which can be produced by irradiating different elements in even low-power nuclear reactors—those which do not qualify for the production of atomic power.

The radioactive elements or radioisotopes to which we have reference did not originate with the development of the nuclear chain reaction. When the first cyclotrons were operated some two decades ago they produced powerful beams of nuclear particles. By exposing an element to a cyclotron beam and allowing it to be a target for a suitable length of time the element could be transmuted or changed into a new and radioactive element. However, this method of radioisotope production was relatively costly and yielded only small amounts of radioactivity.

With the development of the first Oak Ridge pile man had at his disposal a machine which could produce very large quantities of radioisotopes. These are produced simply by inserting the proper element into the reactor and allowing it to be irradiated sufficiently long. Neutrons inside the pile bombard the atoms of the sample changing them into new radioactive atoms. After the war the Army, and then the Atomic Energy Commission, made radioisotopes generally available to science and industry. The Oak Ridge pile became part of an isotope factory and soon over one hundred different radioisotopes were put on sale. The AEC set up a division headed up by Dr. Paul Aebersold to market these radioactive products and to see that their use was encouraged and at the same time restricted so that proper health precautions would be observed in handling them. One of the world's most unusual price lists is that issued by Dr. Aebersold's division. It lists all the many different kinds of radioisotopes for sale and stipulates the cost for a given number of radioactive atoms. The radioisotopes listed may belong to the elements gold, tin, arsenic, sodium, or any of many elements. Each radioisotope has its own particular characteristics or nuclear personality. Some emit radiation that is stopped by a sheet of writing paper; others give off rays which are absorbed in about one hundred sheets of paper, and still others emit radiation that penetrates through even an inch of lead. The first and most easily absorbed radiation we know is a nuclear particle called an alpha particle. The second one with intermediate penetrating power is a beta particle and is simply a high-speed electron such as is emitted by the glowing filament of a radio tube. The third radiation is exactly the same as X-radiation and goes by the name of gamma radiation. When gamma-emitting radioisotopes are shipped from Oak Ridge they are encased in lead shields so that no one would be injured in transporting them. An additional consideration is that they might be put in the same vehicle with photographic film and might badly fog it if not suitably shielded.

Radiations given off by radioisotopes are the valuable attributes which make them so useful in the variety of applications we shall describe in this chapter. Because the rays can penetrate through matter and because instruments like Geiger counters can detect the presence of individual rays it is possible to perform highly unusual experiments with infinitesimal amounts of the radioisotopes. Another feature of radioactive elements is also very important in their usefulness—this is the fact that their radioactivity, or the rate at which radiations are emitted, is not constant but changes as time passes, always decreasing according to the precise laws of physics until finally the initial amount of radioactive material has decayed to such a small amount that it can no longer be detected. Each radioisotope exhibits its own characteristic rate of decay or, more technically, has its own special half life. The latter is simply the time which it takes for the initial amount of radioactivity to decrease to one half its initial value. One radioisotope of the element carbon, for example, has a half life of 5,700 years. This means that if we started out an experiment today then in 5,700 years we would have only half as much radiocarbon left. Some elements like uranium have even longer-lived isotopes, the familiar U-238 having the very long half life of 1.5 billion years. On the other hand some radioisotopes may live for only a fleeting instant. In fact some have been measured to have a half life of only millionths of one second.

The time element becomes very important for radioisotopes which are short-lived. They have to be processed quickly at Oak Ridge and then flown to where they will be used so that enough of the radioactive material will still be on hand with which to perform an experiment. Very often this necessitates around-the-clock operations in the laboratory. It would be nice, as many a bleary-eyed scientist wearied from long hours of work has observed, to have radioactivity which could be turned off and on like an electric light. However, radioactivity is immutable and man has to work with it as best he can.

With this brief technical introduction we shall proceed to see how we can use radioisotopes for man's benefit. To make the discussion orderly we shall divide up the applications for radioactivity into four categories where it is most useful. These are medical science, agriculture, industry, and pure science.

Radioisotopes have proved a great boon to medical science because they have made available to the research worker an extremely sensitive tool for exploring into the inner workings of what takes place inside the human body. Ordinary methods of analysis, such as through chemistry, are not as sensitive as the many radioactive measurements which can be made without disturbing the *status quo* in the body. Furthermore, chemical measurements are often time-consuming and the results are not always clear cut. By using a tiny amount of radioisotope one can trace the course of a fluid or chemical or drug from the time it enters the body until when it is taken by some organ or is finally excreted. For example, some radioactive sodium can be incorporated into sodium chloride—ordinary salt—in which case we speak of a tagged or labeled salt molecule. This radioactive salt can then be mixed with ordinary nonradioactive salt; chemically the two are identical and cannot be distinguished by the body. Once taken into the body one can easily trace the presence of the salt through its radioactivity. It is found, for instance, that within one minute after intake the body may give off perspiration which contains the radioactive molecules of salt. This is just one example of how radioactivity permits quick and convenient study of how the human chemical factory operates. Without the radioactive tagging of the salt there would be no way to chemically distinguish salt added to the body from that which was already inside.

Using radiosodium injected into the blood stream the total volume of the circulating blood can be determined. This is done by taking a small blood sample once the radioactive material has mixed in the bloodstream and then analyzing the extent to which the radioactivity was diluted. Such knowledge of the total volume of blood is useful to doctors especially in studying the treatment of circulatory deficiencies. The radioactive method of quickly determining the flow of blood in the extremities is sometimes of dramatic importance. In a West-Coast accident a woman was severely injured and one leg was so badly mangled that it was felt that amputation was indicated. However, a quick injection of a radioactive salt into the bloodstream was made and a Geiger counter was held over the foot to see if the blood was still circulating through the shattered leg in sufficient volume to forgo the amputation. The subsequent chattering of the Geiger counter showed that circulation was still adequate and the patient was spared the amputation.

Medical diagnosis has been greatly aided by the new radioactive tool especially where doctors can take advantage of the fact that certain elements tend to "lay down" or concentrate in specific body organs. It was found that brain tumors contained tissue which absorbed up to one hundred times more phosphorus than normal healthy brain tissue. By giving a patient an intravenous injection of a solution containing radiophosphorus it is possible to track down the concentration of radioactivity built up in the brain tumor and thus to locate the otherwise undiagnosed tumor. Localizing such brain tumors with this radioisotope technique was greatly facilitated by the development of tiny Geiger counters which could be moved across the surface of the exposed brain and thus used to track down the precise location of the tumor.

Probably the widest use of radioisotopes in diagnosis occurs in the analysis of thyroid abnormalities. The thyroid gland situated at the base of the neck is unusual in that it uses almost all the iodine taken in the body. A healthy thyroid pulls almost eighty times as much iodine from the body's supply as any other body tissue. In cases where there is an overactive thyroid (hyperthyroid condition) the gland absorbs iodine at a faster rate than normal. Where the thyroid is subnormal in activity, a condition known as hypothyroidism, the gland picks up iodine at a slower rate. However, early diagnosis of thyroid malfunction was difficult until a radiotracer technique was perfected. Once a radioactive isotope of iodine was available it was no trick at all to solve the problem for the tagged radioactive iodine behaved exactly as ordinary iodine. A patient could swallow a radioiodine solution, popularly called an atomic cocktail, and then the rate at which his thyroid picked up radioactivity was a measure of the functional state of the gland.

Radioiodine proved useful not only for diagnosing improper functioning of the thyroid but also for therapeutic treatment of hyperthyroidism. In radiotherapy much larger doses of radioisotopes are required than for tracer experiments. Theoretically one could bombard the thyroid gland with an external beam of X-rays but in practice one encounters the difficulty that before these rays hit the thyroid gland they must pass through skin, underlying tissue, and such specialized tissue as in muscles, blood vessels, and nerves. Before enough radiation could be delivered to the thyroid gland other tissue in the vicinity might be overirradiated and injured. Internal treatment with radioiodine, selectively deposited in the thyroid, was a solution which allowed the rays to bombard only the thyroid and very little other tissue. This technique is known as internal therapy. It is often effective in treating thyroid tumors especially in instances where the patient might not be likely to tolerate radical surgery.

Unfortunately, there are not many organs like the thyroid which exhibit a pronounced appetite for a single element and concentrate it so preponderantly. Recently considerable work has been done using radiophosphorus, internally administered, in the treatment of certain types of leukemia, a pathological blood condition in which there is an overly abundant production of white blood cells. The same radioelement may be used to treat polycythemia or overproduction of the red blood cells. In each of these blood diseases the internal treatment with radiophosphorus is useful because the element is to a certain extent selectively laid down in the bone marrow where the blood cells are formed.

Radioisotopes may also be used as a substitute for radium in radiation therapy in the local or external treatment of the body. Here the element cobalt has a radioisotope which is particularly useful as a substitute, for it has essentially the same type of radiation as radium and it has two advantages. For one thing it is cheaper than radium which costs up to $20,000 per gram and it can be made available in large quantity. Most radium sources available in big hospitals are from one to five grams in size. A single radiocobalt source equivalent to 1,000 grams of radium has been ordered for the Oak Ridge Cancer Hospital. Another advantage is that unlike radium which is available only in the form of a salt which is sealed in special containers, radiocobalt can be fashioned in metallic form in a wide variety of shapes and sizes for internal applicators.

In addition to providing the diagnostician and the therapist with new tools, radioisotopes show even greater promise in biological and clinical research. Drugs can be labeled with a radioisotope and their action in the human body studied. Furthermore, better understanding can be obtained as to how the body organs function in health and in disease. Even beyond the direct aid which the radioisotope technique gives to the research worker is the stimulus of joining medical and biological science closer to the physical sciences. This union should reward both richly.

More than 1 billion of the earth's people are estimated to subsist on substandard amounts of food. The rapid growth of the world's population has outpaced man's ability to provide sufficient food for everyone. Indeed, certain islands so teem with millions of inhabitants that even though every available acre of land is cultivated and farmed intensively food production cannot meet the consumer demands. Enhancing man's food supply therefore becomes one of the most important areas of human endeavor. The use of the radiotracer technique can certainly make it possible for man to probe into the fundamentals of the problem of producing more food per acre of arable land.

Just as radioisotopes can be used as tracers in the human body to study the mechanism of circulation and of organ function, they can also be used to study how plants take nourishment from the soil. Agriculture is an age-old art but modern science can now analyze the empirical rules of making land yield plant products to see if the yield per acre can be boosted. Man's oldest industry is not too old to be put under the microscope and improved. In the United States, for example, farmers pay out about $750 million each year for some 15 million tons of fertilizer. Naturally any farmer who pays good money for fertilizer wants it to be used most efficiently by his plant crop. Here is where the radioisotopes may be used to advantage to determine how much of the fertilizer is actually taken up by the plant. Suppose that one wishes to study the efficiency with which corn absorbs a phosphate fertilizer. Radiophosphorus can be added to the normal phosphate in the form of tagged phosphate. The phosphate fertilizer is then spread in the corn field and the rate of uptake of the radioactive fertilizer can be studied quite accurately by measuring the amount of radiophosphorus in the plant. The latter determination can be made with sensitive instruments such as Geiger counters. By studying the rate of fertilizer uptake one can perform many experiments to determine when the fertilizer should be applied, that is, at what stage in the growth cycle of the plant is the fertilizer most needed. In the case of corn it is found that phosphate fertilizer is absorbed most readily during the early phase of the growing cycle. In later stages of the growth cycle the deeper roots of the corn plants take most of their phosphorus from that already in the soil. This contrasts with experience with potatoes where radioisotope studies have shown that these plants continue to draw their phosphorus supply from the applied fertilizer. Tracer technique may also be used to determine just where the fertilizer should be deposited with respect to the seedling so as to produce maximum benefit.

The many agricultural studies which have already been carried out with radioactive tracers have shown that much fertilizer used in the United States has been wasted. A single experiment conducted at North Carolina State College illustrates how fertilizer can be conserved by using it properly. Tracer experiments using radioactive phosphorus incorporated into a phosphate fertilizer showed that applying this nutriment to the surface of the ground proved of little value to the growth of tobacco plants. As a result the phosphate content of the tobacco fertilizer was eliminated. This added up to a saving of over 4,000 tons of superphosphate for the state of North Carolina.

Studies such as those just described are of obvious practical importance to farmers. However, there are many experiments in progress which, while they are not so demonstrably of practical importance, will probably contribute far more to plant science and to the enrichment of man's food supply. These researches are conducted to study the fundamental process of photosynthesis— that all important process whereby plant tissue is synthesized. All land plants and algae act as microscopic factories running on three basic ingredients: water, carbon dioxide, and sunlight. The sun supplies the energy which fuses the basic ingredients together to form energy-rich carbohydrates. The mystery of how green plants grow has intrigued scientists for generations and now the use of radioisotopes provides a tool for prying into one of nature's most closely guarded secrets. Understanding of the fundamental mechanism of the process of photosynthesis may make it possible for man to take giant strides in making more food available.

Even though plants are individually good converters of the sun's energy, only a small fraction of the sun's energy is stored up in plant growth. Chlorophyll, now widely used in chewing gum and a variety of items, is the vital green substance in plants which makes it possible to use sunlight as a source of energy to convert carbon dioxide and water into energy-rich carbohydrates. When this is in the form of an edible food the energy is released within the human body and serves to provide heat to keep the body warm and energy to do work. When in the form of a woody substance (tree) it serves as a source of heat energy. Ferns and vegetable matter which grew millions of years ago under tropical conditions provided the source of the petroleum and coal for man's factories and furnaces of today. The total energy which the sun delivers to the earth's surface each year is unbelievably immense. The clue to tapping more of this vast store of available energy lies in better understanding of the basic role of photosynthesis, and radioactive tracers can do much to provide the clue.

Anyone who has ever been on a farm knows the constant battle which the farmer must wage against plant pests and diseases. It has been estimated that the ravages of both do about $8 billion in damage each year. The most spectacular devastation comes as a result of invading hordes of locusts, grasshoppers, or other insects which virtually strip the fields of their green mantle. Less obvious but more important because of their widespread occurrence are the less wholesale invasions of insects and plant fungi, molds, and rusts.

Modern fungicides and insecticides like DDT and others have been developed to combat plant pests and diseases but these are only partial solutions. They make possible a kind of holding operation against the inroads on the crops. New resistant strains of fungi and new insecticide-resistant pests develop to plague the farmer. Radioisotopes make it possible to study the action of fungicides and insecticides and to know about how the lethal action of the sprays and dusts takes place. In addition the tracer technique is a wonderful means of testing the relative efficiency of new chemicals in their ability to kill fungi and insects.

The migrations of insects have often proved as puzzling to scientists as they have proved abominable to farmers. Relatively little was known of the specific habits of many insects because of the obvious difficulty in tagging each insect, following its peregrinations, and then locating its habitats. Here, again, radioisotopes proved of value. An experiment with ordinary blowflies will illustrate how individual insects can be tagged and identified. A test colony of some 15,000 flies was bred and when ready for experiment they were made very thirsty by being denied water for several days. Then they were dined on a radioactive phosphorus solution and when they had drunk their fill they were released. Fly traps, baited with decomposed liver, were set up at points up to four, and later twelve miles from the original colony. Blowflies collected at each trap were examined for radioactivity and counted. The flies showed unexpected power of flight for they migrated a distance of up to four miles the first day and up to eight miles the second day. Experiments such as these make it possible to study the life habits of insects in a more quantitative manner than would be possible without the use of radioisotopes.

In studying the metabolism of nutriments in plants a technique known as radioautography has been used with great success. We may use the example of the tomato plant to illustrate this technique. In tracing how the tomato, itself, utilizes phosphorus a radioactive phosphate fertilizer may be introduced into the soil around the plant roots. Then after enough time has elapsed for the fruit to concentrate out sufficient amounts of the radioactive material the tomato may be removed and sectioned. A piece of sensitive photographic emulsion is placed almost in contact with the tomato slice and allowed to remain there long enough for the radiation from the absorbed radiophosphorus to register on the photographic film. When removed and developed the film shows a picture of how the radioactivity was distributed in the tomato. Where large amounts of radiophosphorus concentrated in the tomato the film will be blackest and correspondingly where there was no appreciable radioactivity the film will be clear. Thus one gets a radiopicture of how the phosphorus gets distributed in the tomato. This radiographic technique turns out to be a convenient and useful way of determining the way in which certain minerals are taken up within the plant.

The new tracer technique has also been used successfully in the field of animal husbandry. Those who have to pay for the feeding of livestock, including the ultimate consumer, should be anxious to cut the feed costs as much as possible. The objective in raising cattle or poultry may be somewhat formally stated as improving the efficiency with which a pound of feed is converted into marketable meat or poultry. One must understand the basic physiology of the animal if it is to be made into a more efficient food producer. Thus basic studies on animal physiology which might at first seem to be of interest only to the pure scientist may result in new feeding techniques or in the breeding of new animal types. Radioisotopes are already showing great promise in experiments which will give the livestock producer more meat on the hoof for each pound of cattle feed consumed. Furthermore, the time required for fattening animals to marketable size may be considerably reduced if one can take advantage of certain biochemicals and vitamins as additives to animal feed.

Extensive experiments have been undertaken to see what is the direct effect of nuclear radiation on plants and animals. It has been known since the turn of the century that X-rays and radium rays can cause drastic changes in the growth pattern of animals and plants. In general it is found that radiation has a harmful effect or a retarding influence on growth. Too much radiation kills off plants. Furthermore, excessive amounts of radiation tend to cause abnormal and nonbeneficial changes in the plants. This being true one might ask why the Atomic Energy Commission currently sponsors so much research on the effect of radiation on plants. There are a number of very good reasons why this work is both necessary and valuable. In the first place increasing amounts of radioactivity are being let loose into the world. In the event of an atomic war enormously larger amounts of radiation would bombard our plains and forests. It is therefore of vital interest to the nation that we know as much as possible about any effects, beneficial or detrimental, which radiation may have upon living things. Secondly, if we understand how radiation injures plants and animals we may be able to put this knowledge to good use in making radiation benefit growing things. For example, it may be that properly controlled doses of radiation might stimulate plant growth. Finally, we may be able to use radiation to produce genetic changes so that new strains of plants with superior characteristics may be evolved. One can think of strains of wheat which would be more resistant to rusts and other wheat enemies. An X-ray-induced mutant was used in the early development of a mold for producing the valuable antibiotic penicillin.

In connection with the direct effects of radiation on food products there has been a recent development which shows considerable promise. It is the use of intense beams of high-speed electrons to irradiate such items as fruits, milk, and biological drugs. Passage of the radiation through the material which is contained in a sealed package of some type kills or inhibits the growth of organisms which produce deterioration and decay of the food or drug product. The hope would be that this technique might make it possible to sterilize milk without flash heating or to keep milk fresh longer. The hope is also that elaborate canning and deep-freezing techniques for food might be dispensed with, provided of course that the radiation sterilization does not change the flavor of the product. In this connection, one of my friends from Puerto Rico made the personal observation that irradiation of a "poor grade" of rum converted it into quite a tasty product. This new preservative process must still be considered in the cocoon stage of development and it is still too early to make predictions about it. However, experiments with fruits and vegetables yield dramatic results. An irradiated apple retained its firmness and appearance without visible sign of deterioration even though it was kept at room temperature for three months. This spectacular result needs a strong additive of caution, however, for before any of these products would be marketed it must be conclusively demonstrated to the Food and Drug Administration as well as to the U.S. Public Health Service that they are not harmful. The possibility cannot be ruled out that the irradiation technique involves the production of substances which are carcinogenic (cancer producing).

We shall now turn our attention to industry and to commercial processes and see how atomic science stands to contribute here. To date American industry has been quite slow to adopt radioisotopes either as a tool for research or as a means of industrial control. There are probably less than fifty firms of any consequence which have undertaken to use nuclear radiation in their plants. This reluctance to accept a promising new technique may be chalked up to the relative newness of the radiotracer method and to the notion that radioactive materials are too much of a hazard to plant personnel to warrant their use. Recognizing this attitude on the part of industry the Atomic Energy Commission launched a program in co-operation with the Stanford Research Institute to explore the possible uses for the atom in commerce and industry.

At the outset it must be acknowledged even by enthusiasts that radioactive materials and techniques are not going to revolutionize industry but they will provide highly useful tools to supplement conventional instrumentation and techniques in use today. Tiny invisible amounts of radioactive materials can be used to run control checks on the chemical composition of huge batches of molten steel, to measure and control the thickness of tissue-thin films of plastics, and to determine the flow of liquids through long pumping lines. They will make it possible to develop new industrial processes and to improve existing ones. We shall describe rather briefly a number of illustrations of the way in which industry can use radioisotopes.

In many large-scale industrial processes such as the making of steel formidable amounts of material are contained in one melt and it is always important to maintain an accurate check on the chemical composition of the molten mass. Adding a trace of radiosulfur to approximately twelve tons of mixed coal in one run allowed technicians to assay how much of the sulfur in the produced steel arose from the coke and what fraction was contributed by the iron, itself. The use of a small amount of radiophosphorus added to the melt allows one to keep accurate track of the phosphorus impurities in the batch of steel throughout the steel-making process. Another radioisotope—carbon 14—proves of value in steel making because of the importance of carbon in steel. For example, radiocarbon can be used to find out just how carbon diffuses the steel. In general, the radiotracer technique is well adapted to helping the metallurgist understand and control the complex changes which occur in metal production and in the manufacture of alloys.

Engineers concerned with the design of moving parts in internal combustion engines have used radioactivity to measure the extent of frictional wear to a degree that is rather astonishing. For example, piston-ring wear has been accurately measured by taking the piston rings and sending them to Oak Ridge. There they are irradiated by exposing them to neutron bombardment in the Oak Ridge nuclear reactor. After "cooking" in this atomic furnace for a suitable length of time, dependent upon the requirements of the experiment, the piston rings are removed and sent to the engineers in shielded packages. Then the rings are fitted into the cylinders of an engine and run in for different lengths of time. As the motor is run tiny particles of metal are worn off the piston ring and collected in the lubricating oil. By using Geiger counters to measure the radioactivity of the lubricant at various times the piston-ring wear can be easily and accurately determined. The sensitivity of the method used in these friction studies is such that as little as one-hundred-billionth of one ounce of steel can be determined to wear off a single moving part. Furthermore, one can easily use the same method to investigate how efficient various types of lubricants are in reducing engine friction.

Petroleum scientists use radiocarbon and other tracers to study the fundamental and very complex processes which take place in the big cracking units where gasoline is produced. Looking forward to the future when much gasoline may be made synthetically, research experts are probing into the workings of the process whereby coal and natural gas can be fused together to form gasoline. In the field, the possibility suggests itself that radioactive material may be injected into oil beds to discover the extent of the oil field. This might be done by shooting a large amount of a radioactive element into one oil well and then examining the pumpings from nearby oil wells to test for evidence of the same radioactivity. Such data would indicate something of the nature of the underground strata and the subterranean connections between oil wells.

While we are on the topic of oil, one very interesting and novel application of radioisotopes deserves mention. A single interstate pumping line may be used to handle the transport of different grades of crude petroleum or batches owned by different companies. Chemically these may be indistinguishable or identified only with difficulty. Since each batch has to be shunted at the end of the line to separate tanks or refineries it becomes essential that the operator at the terminal point know when to turn the proper valves. In the past this problem was not readily solved but by using radioactive materials it is solved quite easily. The technique used is to inject into the pipe line between the different batches of oil some short-lived radioisotope. This serves as a marker for the operator at the end of the line and when his radioactive detectors pick up the signal he can turn the valves which divert the oil to the proper places. Furthermore, the progress of the oil in being pumped across country can be watched by having Geiger counters record the passage of the radioactive material at each booster pumping station.

Another application is suggested by the previous illustration. It is the use of a radioactive material to indicate the height of a liquid inside a metal container. Where the liquids inside are corrosive or high pressures prohibit the use of observation ports · a sealed float can be used together with a radioactive source emitting gamma rays. The latter penetrate through the container and by running a Geiger counter up and down the side of the tank the height of the liquid level inside can easily be ascertained. Using the same principle some clever technicians rigged up a device to cause elevators to stop exactly at the right floor level. A beam of radiation emitted by a radioactive source attached to the elevator shaft served to define the position of the floor level.

Rubber chemists have found that the use of radiosulfur is very valuable in the analysis of the intricate steps involved in the vulcanization of rubber. Sulfur is known to be extremely important in this highly useful process but for many years its real function has been rather mysterious. Chemists are hopeful that radiosulfur will dissipate much of the mystery still enshrouding the vulcanization process.

Radioisotopes are also expected to play an important role in the plastics industry. This relatively new industry has boomed enormously since the war as is evident, for example, in the field of synthetic fibers which now offer serious competition with cotton and wool in the garment business. Chemical processes involved in making rayon, nylon, dacron, orlon and all the other wonder fibres are complex and need delicate control to insure a high quality uniformity to the finished product. Radiocarbon and other isotopes may be expected to contribute to understanding of the chemical processes involved in making these new synthetics and they may also be used to actually control production.

An easily visualized illustration of production control in the plastics field is found in the manufacture of thin plastic film. Such films are used for a thousand and one purposes ranging from use in shower curtains to packaging food. It is important that the plastic sheets be of uniform thickness but this presents a problem in making accurate thickness gages. Ordinarily a mechanical instrument presses the film between two tips of a micrometer but this has the disadvantage of being inaccurate and injurious to a fast moving sheet of plastic speeding off the rollers of the production line. Here the radioactive thickness gage came into its own. A radioactive measuring device in use at the Goodyear Tire and Rubber Company at Akron, Ohio, serves to detect the radiation from a radiocarbon source. Between the source and the detector runs the rapidly moving plastic film. Dependent upon the thickness of the film a number of radioparticles will be transmitted which is greater if the film is thinner. The radiation meter therefore serves as a measuring device to indicate the thickness of the film. It can be calibrated so that it will read to an accuracy of one-hundred-thousandth of an inch. Thus even though nothing mechanically touches the speeding film the thickness can be measured accurately. Moreover, the measuring meter can be hooked up with an amplifier and electronic control so that the speed of the rollers, and therefore the thickness of the film, can be controlled. What this means is that the entire film production line can be made automatic.

Vast quantities of fission products accumulate annually in our huge production plants at Hanford as the result of the operation of plutonium-producing reactors. These are waste products which are essentially an expensive nuisance to the Atomic Energy Commission. Waste solutions contain large quantities of radioactive material and it is hoped that some of this may be salvaged and used by industry as an intense source of radiation. One possibility is that such powerful radiation might be used for radiography as a substitute for radium in inspecting thick metal castings and fabricated items for flaws. Another possibility is that such sources might be used to sterilize food products as we discussed earlier in this chapter. To a minor degree some of the fission products will find useful application in such miscellaneous devices as static eliminators and in fluorescent lamps.

As an indication of the growth of a new industry unique to the atomic field there is the spectacular rise of the radiation instrument business. I recall that at the end of the war our laboratory had been engaged in the small-scale production of Geiger-counter and other radiation-detection instruments. There were at that time less than a handful of companies in the business of making such instruments for there was a very limited demand for them. It was part of an assignment I had to make a survey of the radiation field, dig up companies which might be interested in getting into the field, and interest them in taking on new business. Subsequently the Atomic Energy Commission encouraged the growth of the industry and today there are over seventy-five companies in the field with annual sales already edging toward the $10 million mark. These organizations range from large outfits like Tracerlab, Inc., of Boston to very small companies with less than a dozen employees.

The last type of applications we shall consider are those specific to pure science. Since most of the examples which might be given might be of too limited interest to nonscientists we shall describe only one illustration of a scientific application of radioisotope technique. This is the use of a radioactive method for measuring time perfected by Dr. Willard F. Libby at the University of Chicago. Dr. Libby discovered that when cosmic rays bombard the earth's atmosphere they convert some of the nitrogen in the air to radiocarbon. This particular form of carbon has a radioactivity with a half life of 5,700 years. Growing plants incorporate some of the radiocarbon in the process of photosynthesis so that wood and fibers contain a small amount of the special form of carbon. The uptake of radiocarbon stops when the plant dies. Thereafter the ratio of the radioactive carbon (which constantly vanishes through decay) to the normal or non-radioactive carbon changes as time goes on. It is by measuring this ratio that scientists can determine how much time has elapsed since the death of the plant. This set of facts might seem to have interest only for long-haired professors but actually as it turned out they had much wider significance. With as little as an ounce of some carbon-containing relic of the past Dr. Libby has been able to measure the amount of radiocarbon in the sample and by direct calculations deduce to what period in history the sample belongs. Using a piece of charred bone from an ancient cave, Dr. Libby was able to date the origin of the sample as being 9,000 years B.C. This is an example of how what was originally the object of a scientist's curiosity became a valuable tool for archeologists. Many analyses have been performed on historic artifacts, and arguments about the periods to which they belong have been resolved by the impersonal and unerring Geiger counter.

Some measure of the over-all popularity of radioisotopes is given by a few statistics. By the beginning of 1953 the AEC had shipped from Oak Ridge a total of almost 30,000 separate consignments of radioisotopes. There are about 1,000 isotope users in the United States and in addition to this domestic consumption the AEC made shipments to thirty-three foreign countries. The annual shipments of these radioactive materials continue to increase each year as more and more individuals learn the technique of using them. To assist in the learning process a special school has been established at Oak Ridge, and there qualified persons may receive indoctrination into the proper use of the radioisotopes. In terms of the dollars spent in this new field it is encouraging that this whole operation costs the taxpayer very little money. Isotope users pay their own way although those working on cancer research are granted a partial subsidy to aid in their work.

The Atomic Energy Commission's program for the production and distribution of radioactive materials has been a well-founded operation which for the relatively small amount of money spent has yielded good dividends and promises to yield even more. So far it is the only real peacetime benefit of atomic energy which has emerged in the Atomic Age. It is worth noting that the money spent by the AEC for radioisotopes amounts to about .1 per cent of its total expenditures.

11

SECRECY AND THE ATOM

In the United States we have built up an atomic wall to keep our A-bomb and its secrets safe from Soviet eyes. Certainly no loyal American would question this objective. Without doubt, there are things about our atomic program which the Russians would give a great deal to know. But we have gone off in the wrong direction, announcing with a fanfare those bits of information most useful to a potential enemy, and jealously guarding— to our own detriment—the things he can find out for himself. In many respects this policy has been like worrying over small leaks in a dam when the floodgates have been opened.

During the war when I worked behind the barbed wire and sealed doors of our atomic project I was, like all scientists, accustomed to the tight lid of wartime secrecy which had been slammed down on our work. On August 8, 1945, just three days after the first A-bomb was dropped on Japan I got a taste of what was in store for me during "peacetime"! I received a crisply worded letter from Oak Ridge which announced: "You are advised that official public statements and releases comprise permissible limits of disclosure of information at this time. Independent publications, addresses, or advertising by individuals or groups cannot be released without prior clearance." Thereafter everything I wrote as a government employee was subject to the censor's heavy blue pencil for "clearance" meant official scrutiny of every written word.

After years of secrecy scientists could scarcely believe that they could talk about atomic energy in public subject, of course, to censorship. An official report of the Manhattan Project, known as the Smyth Report, was quickly published after V-J day. This much disputed account of the atomic program undoubtedly told the Soviets items of interest to them but one wonders how much more it told them than what they had learned through their espionage. One very valuable result of publishing the Smyth Report is generally overlooked. The publication served to draw a chalk line for American scientists, marking off the area which could be talked about in public. So that in this sense the report represented a wise and reasonable solution to the problem of releasing information to the public and making sure that scientists would not divulge additional technical data.

Although American work on the A-bomb remained a deep dark secret to most people throughout the war it is wrong to believe that only a handful of people knew what was going on. The big tip-off came in 1940 when suddenly everything connected with the word "atom" disappeared from the scientific literature. Anyone who was slightly curious about this untimely demise of atomic energy could have ferreted out the reason in no time at all. He needed only to make the rounds of the big universities and inquire as to the whereabouts of Fermi, Oppenheimer, or any one of many other nuclear scientists. Fermi's whereabouts would then be found to coincide with that of other top-notch physicists at one of the Manhattan Project's closely guarded sites. From there on the chase would be narrowed down and the secret would have been very obvious. But one did not even have to move out of home to discover the big secret. You could have ordered a copy of the Minerals Yearbook from the Government Printing Office and on page 828 of the 1943 edition you would have found the big secret spelled out: "Uranium production in 1943 was greatly stimulated by a Government program having materials priority over all other minerals procurement, but most of the facts were buried in War Department secrecy. . . . Most of the 1943 uranium supply was used by physics laboratories for research on uranium isotopes as a source of energy."

Following the war a curious thing happened. A myth about there being an atomic secret was born. Congressmen urged great caution upon those entrusted with the security of atomic work so that *the secret* of the A-bomb would not be given to a foreign country. Here one thing should be made crystal clear: *there is no secret to the A-bomb*. Once there was a secret but that went up in the smoke of the bomb explosion over Hiroshima. As General Groves, himself, once testified before Congress: "The big secret was really something we could not keep quiet and that was the fact that the thing went off." This, assuredly, was the big secret. To be sure we had lots of little secrets but there is no use in pretending (although we still do) that these were really something you could hope to keep from an enemy.

The little secrets were things which any scientist be he German,

Russian, or American would uncover when he went into his laboratory and subjected Mother Nature to rigorous cross-examination in the form of well-thought-out experiments. Nature cannot withhold a secret from an intelligent scientist. Regardless of his nationality he wins from an experiment the same answer as his fellow scientist on the other side of the world. This is just another way of saying that science is universal or as Professor Einstein put it: "Scientists are an international community." Science knows no restraint in the form of an international boundary line. Men on each side of the line are just as free to probe out the secrets of nature. The history of science is replete with examples of scientists who, though separated by thousands of miles, independently made the same discovery. We noted this in the case of the American physicist E. M. McMillan and the Russian scientist Veksler, both of whom discovered the way to make a supercyclotron accelerate particles to ten times the energy previously attainable. The fact that science is not a one-way street for any one nation should require no further substantiation.

What, then, were the secrets of our atomic work which we were supposed to protect after V-J day if the big secret was out and the little secrets were something any good scientist could discover? The answer is that they were secrets of technology and industry best summed up in the phrase "industrial know-how." This is what General Groves called the real secret of the atomic project when he stated that: "The real secret of this development does not lie in the work that was done at Los Alamos, which was the development of the bomb, itself, it was in the preparation of the material that was the hard job." This is an extremely important conclusion for it means that the secret was not a bomb secret but a production secret.

We had secrets, all right, but they did not involve the principles of nature available to scientists everywhere. From the Soviet viewpoint the things about the U. S. atomic project which loom as most important are the kinds of weapons we are developing and the time scale for those weapons—in short, the "what" and "when" of our weaponry. Such information would enable the men in the Kremlin to prepare their defenses, and perhaps develop weapons to match ours.

Our real secret weapon was our well-known American genius for mass production. It still is the big secret of our atomic work. American technological know-how and American ability to mass produce made Oak Ridge and Hanford possible. But everyone knows that there is no secret to a Detroit assembly line; you are even invited by the management to tour the plants.

America, however, was in no mood to look very closely into the matter of whether there really were any atomic secrets. It preferred to be victimized by the hypnotic effect of secrecy into believing that it could maintain an atomic monopoly. Secrecy therefore became synonymous with security. The newly established Atomic Energy Commission, being largely the brain child of scientists who had insisted that there were no atomic secrets, might have been expected to fight back against the forces which sought greater secrecy. It came as a disappointment to scientists that the AEC did not fight back but knuckled under and was soon imitating the security measures of General Groves. However, most scientists were by this time immersed in peacetime research and enchanted with the tranquility of the campus. Moreover, not a few were camping on the AEC's doorstep asking for research funds. So while scientists may have been perturbed by the AEC's adherence to military-type security they did not protest. In all fairness to both the scientists and the atomic agency, the latter did adopt a policy of publishing technical data of interest to scientists. In general the AEC has done a commendable job in issuing technical reports. But in the field of public information the AEC badly fumbled the ball.

Put in the bluntest of words, the AEC is scared to death of the military and of Congress. From personal experience where I have submitted documents for clearance I have found that too often the attitude of AEC officials has been, "Will this information if published invoke the wrath of Capitol Hill or of the Pentagon?" To such a policy, which was easily discerned by the nature of the information under discussion, I always objected very vigorously, demanding that my writings be reviewed purely on a security basis. I recall one rather heated discussion when I was trying to get a *Collier's* article on atomic artillery cleared. It had been in the Pentagon for several months. I discovered that the military were not so much concerned with security as they were with saving a publicity nest-egg for themselves. Pentagon censors objected to my stating the caliber of the atomic howitzer as about a foot in diameter; I was then shocked to see photographs of the gun in the newspaper revealing the exact dimensions of the weapon.

The United States continued to slumber on believing in its invincibility through exclusive possession of A-secrets and thus the A-bomb. Then, on September 23, 1949, President Truman announced, "We have evidence that within recent weeks an atomic explosion occurred in the U.S.S.R." The news came just before the World Series and the nation seemed little shocked and more interested in baseball. Then, too, there were the doubting Thomases and columnists who took advantage of the peculiar wording of the announcement to infer that Russia had not tested an A-bomb but had suffered an accident in one of its atomic plants. This was just wishful thinking for the information upon which the President had based his announcement was very conclusive. Russia had tested a bona fide A-bomb of roughly the same size and type as we exploded over Nagasaki. Had this information reached the United States through ordinary intelligence sources one would be justified in doubting it but the news of the event was picked up by the eyes and ears of sensitive instruments more reliable than those of human beings. Instruments have been called the extended fingers of the scientist and in this snooping operation they reached across the seas and ferreted out information which the Soviets obviously wished to conceal.

Just how do the instruments of science become the super-detectives of the atomic age? As the *New York Times* explained it, "No A-bombs can be exploded anywhere in the world without leaving telltale radioactive signs in the atmosphere. Around Russia's periphery the air is 'monitored.' There is always some radioactivity in the air, but the slightest excess of radioactive particles will be detected by sensitive instruments like Geiger counters." That is about as much as I can say until the wraps are taken off the secret project which was set up to detect the Russian bomb tests.

I recall a letter in which David Lilienthal, anticipating the detection of the first Russian bomb, declared that this event should be the signal for a drastic increase in the nation's military preparedness. This foresight was not shared by the nation's military leaders. What is more disconcerting is that the over-all planning in the Pentagon had been based upon the Russians getting their first bomb at least two years later. Despite this abrupt change in the Russian timetable our military program was not stepped up. Instead, it was held at a constant level, then about $12 billion, and attempts were made to cut this back.

Gradually, the truth about the first Soviet A-bomb infused

through Washington. It became apparent that the United States had lost its monopoly on atomic weapons just as scientists had predicted this would happen. The first phase of the atomic arms race ended with the successful detonation of the first Soviet A-bomb. To many it seemed incredible that a country like Russia could achieve this success in such a short time. I recall that almost everyone, except Irving Langmuir, predicted that it would take the Soviets a long time to produce their first bomb. In this respect we gave the enemy the most precious gift that it is possible to give—namely, underestimating his ability. We sadly underestimated Russia. We exaggerated the difficulty of making an A-bomb perhaps partly to gratify our own national ego and partly to put further into the future the time when we would have to worry about the Russian A-bomb.

Early in 1950 Dr. Klaus Fuchs, chief of the Theoretical Physics Division at Britain's principal atomic energy laboratory, was arrested on charges that he had deliberately passed on highly classified atomic data to Soviet agents. This news shocked American scientists who had known Fuchs as a quiet, highly capable physicist at the Los Alamos Laboratory. Almost at once it led to the conclusion that Dr. Fuchs had given the A-bomb to the Soviets. Now there should be no mistake about the nature of the Fuchs disclosure. Fuchs did give very important atomic data to the Soviets. While at our weapons laboratory in New Mexico he had access to almost all the data about the A-bomb. In transmitting these data to the Russians he undoubtedly gave them much useful information. But it is utterly inane to conclude that passing on technical data about the fabrication of an atomic weapon is the same as giving the weapon to the Soviets. It is also ridiculous to maintain that the Fuchs betrayal of our secrets allowed the Russians to get the A-bomb years ahead of time.

We have already emphasized the point, using a quotation from General Groves, that the big task in the Manhattan Project was the building of huge plants to produce bomb material. Scientists at Los Alamos were ready to test the first A-bomb months before the huge plants at Oak Ridge and Hanford had produced their first product sufficient for an A-bomb. Thus, the critical factor in determining when our own A-project paid off was not a weapons problem but a production problem.

This means that Fuchs did not give the A-bomb to the Soviets nor did he save them years in producing the first one. No one could have given the A-bomb to the Soviets not even General Groves. That is, not unless he had gone completely mad and had shipped the material for an A-bomb to Russia. Even so this would have given them only one bomb. To produce the U-235 and plutonium required for their atomic stockpile the Soviets had to build huge plants just as we did. We beguiled ourselves when we were overawed by the thought of spending $2 billion for the Manhattan Project. This was only a small fraction, actually well under 1 per cent, of the cost of World War II. There should have been no reason to believe that the men in the Kremlin would be held to allocating only this amount to their own A-project. Without having to worry about a budget-minded Congress the Kremlin can arbitrarily divert from the national economy any percentage effort that it desires. The fact that the first Russian bomb came in such a short time is a clear indication that the Soviets attach great importance to it.

Almost two years after their first atomic test, the Soviets detonated two more A-bombs. This time when President Truman announced that the atomic explosions had been detected his assertion was verified by Mr. Stalin who said: "Indeed, a test was recently made by us on a type of atom bomb." Clearly, the tempo of the atomic arms race had stepped up.

One would have expected that since the Russians had tested their own A-bomb that many things which we had held secret would then have been released to the American people. This, after all, would only be logical since it would be incredible that the Soviets would have been able to actually explode a bomb successfully without having discovered the very same things we did. But the Atomic Energy Commission did not release such information. Once or twice its chairman, Gordon Dean, intimated that new data would be released but nothing thereafter came of this. All of this clutching at evaporated secrets must be attributed to AEC obeisance to the Congressional view that "we should not tell anything to the Russians." And meanwhile it was of little concern that the American people were not informed on this most vital of all subjects. This myopic policy had all the earmarks of a game of Blindman's Buff. The American people could not be told about the very thing they were expected to defend against. Consider just one example in the area of atomic defense. There has been much talk about the danger to the United States of A-bombs smuggled into our cities there to be exploded at some predetermined time. In the event that there was to be a city-wide search for such a planted A-bomb what would the hunters seek? Should they look for something the size of a shoebox or a piano crate? Should they carry Geiger counters to ferret out the weapon? The answer was not forthcoming. Government officials withheld all information about the size, weight, or shape of the bomb. Now surely the Russians, having tested their own A-bombs and having been granted a look at ours, courtesy of Dr. Fuchs, know how big the bomb is. Certainly, we are not keeping this secret from the Soviets.

Just as A-secrets loomed large in the public mind, now H-secrets loom even larger. And just as there was an A-traitor in Dr.

Fuchs there is, or it is generally imagined that there is, an H-traitor. Dr. Bruno Pontecorvo, Italian-born physicist, has been labeled as the man who gave our hydrogen bomb secrets to the Soviets. On a supposed vacation to Italy in October, 1950, Dr. Pontecorvo suddenly flew to Helsinki with his family and then disappeared behind the Iron Curtain. He had visited U.S. atomic laboratories during the war and afterward had served as a physicist at the Chalk River site in Canada where he did research in cosmic rays. This research he continued when he moved to Harwell, the major British atomic center. It is not generally known that Dr. Pontecorvo did not have access to U.S. weapon research and certainly not to the results of the Eniwetok atomic tests which were so fundamental to the success of the H-bomb. He did have access to data about nuclear reactors, more so than Dr. Fuchs, and to some data about tritium, the critical H-bomb ingredient, but this does not mean that he was thus in a position to give the H-bomb to the Soviets. There is no basic secret to the H-bomb and it is childish to suppose that any policy of secrecy on the hydrogen bomb could prevent the Soviets from developing this superweapon.

In defense of those who keep the secrets or lay down the rules for keeping them it may be said that there is always the question of determining how much your adversary knows. Admittedly, this is something which evades evaluation for many things which go on inside the Iron Curtain are completely sealed off from our intelligence sources. Therefore, the men who wield the thick blue pencil of the censor say, "Since we do not know for certain that the enemy knows this piece of information, let's play it safe by not telling him." There would be no harm in this policy of playing it safe if in the process we did not hurt ourselves. But we are hurting our own progress and we do severe harm to our democratic machinery when we wrap a cloak of secrecy around anything as important as atomic energy. The latter point is undoubtedly the most important of all.

Our democracy is founded upon the principle of free and open discussion of all public issues. The people of the United States raise their voices and make known their views in the Town Hall meeting and thus serve to determine national policy. If the tradition of the town meeting is flaunted and decisions are made in secret by the few then the policies which evolve are not truly those of a democracy. It is the totalitarian state which operates behind locked doors without regard for public opinion. Secrecy is the chosen instrument of the dictatorship. Thus when we adopt the tactics of the totalitarian state we cripple the most basic of all mechanisms by which democracy functions.

The ongrowth of secrecy in government has assumed vast proportions in the past decade. It is by no means confined to atomic energy although it receives greatest specific emphasis in this field. The evil poison of secrecy has penetrated to almost every nook and cranny of bureaucracy. One cannot walk into the offices of a single government agency without being confronted by rows of heavy file safes crammed with thousands of documents stamped restricted, confidential, secret, or top secret. In the Pentagon alone there are thousands of massive steel safes which every work day some thousands of people have to laboriously open and close, nudging the dials into their proper combinations. The formal mechanism for handling these classified documents, secreting them in safes, logging them in and out of message centers, and transmitting them through secure channels is a time-consuming and expensive one. It slows down the wheels of government which do not enjoy any great reputation for spinning rapidly. Why then do so many government agencies adopt such restrictive security practices especially in areas where the national security is not involved?

The answer to this question can be given very bluntly and very honestly. Very few government officials welcome criticism of work under their jurisdiction. Stamping a paper "Secret" is a wonderful administrative invention for it immediately isolates it and the matter involved from public criticism. It must be pointed out here that there is no penalty whatsoever for over-classifying a document. A clerk who arbitrarily affixes the red ink of "Secret" or "Confidential" stamps to a paper is never subject to discipline if it should turn out that the paper contained nothing more than an office memorandum of a change in telephone number. Incidentally, it is something of a shock to many persons to discover that even telephone directories in some Washington agencies are classified "Restricted." Secrecy has become a contagion that has spread throughout officialdom. Agencies have been quick to succumb to this disease which induces a pleasant euphoria and acts as a solid shield to prevent outside criticism. Officials smugly entrenched behind a wall of secrecy do not need to worry about debating the wisdom of their policies. They can commit the most glaring errors, misuse public funds, and virtually get away with murder without suffering the slightest embarrassment. Who is to question what is done within the secret area? Within a single agency self-criticism is extremely rare and between government agencies information is divided into leak-proof compartments.

Theoretically, compartmenting information, like dividing up a ship into watertight sections, is supposed to make for greater security. Ubiquitous spies may be able to break into one compartment but the multiplicity of these is supposed to frustrate complete espionage. This is all very true but it has great disadvantages. To illustrate—let us continue the marine analogy. A ship with many watertight compartments cannot be sunk readily but if the compartments are made so that the engine room cannot communicate with the ship's captain things will get into a frightful mess. Yet setting information into distinct categories and isolating these one from another has the effect of keeping the right hand from knowing what the left hand is doing. This was done in the Manhattan Project. Scientists at Oak Ridge were kept in ignorance of what was going on at Los Alamos and so on.

The Army was not too successful in excommunicating scientists. A kind of scientific smuggling was undertaken to break through the bulwarks of the secrecy compartments. Dr. Leo Szilard, one of the first to recognize the military value of the atom, neatly describes this bootleg operation:

Hardly a week passed that somebody did not come to my office at Chicago from somewhere wanting to convey a piece of information to which I was not entitled. They usually said that they did not ask me to conceal the fact that I came into possession of this information, all they asked was that I conceal from the Army the fact that they were the persons who had given it to me. These men went to much trouble not in order to please me but because they thought I needed the information for my work.

It is impossible to subdivide a scientific project into airtight compartments and produce anything but mediocrity and stagnation. A scientist is not like a carpenter who can be turned out to work with a few specific tools of his trade. Very often it happens that the least likely ideas and developments are the ones which contribute the most to the progress of a scientific development. It is the cross-fertilization of new ideas and novel techniques which often causes a science to spurt ahead with unexpected speed. Deny this science free access to the stimulus of other fields and you stymie its evolution.

In Chapter 10 we gave a number of illustrations of recent advances in biology and medicine. This progress would not have been possible had knowledge of radioactivity been denied to those who studied what happens in cells and tissue. The physicist was able to make valuable contributions to the biologist and in return he learned things of use to his own work. One can not predict what information a scientist will need in his own work. A man doing research in radar may need data from a meteorologist in order to study the propagation of radar waves in the earth's atmosphere. Once a new technique or a new instrument is perfected it must be made freely available for it is just as impossible to predict where the completed invention will be most useful. For example, the basic research on high-frequency radiation before the war was converted into radar apparatus during the war and afterward found application in such diverse uses as guiding ships into fog-bound harbors, bringing aircraft in safely when airports were weathered in, and in accelerating atomic particles in supercyclotrons. Thus when the bonds of secrecy are put around a project and crisscross it into airtight compartments isolating it from itself as well as from the outside world the progress within the secret area is impeded. This is always a danger inherent in secrecy. You lose the very thing that you are trying to attain—namely, an advantage over the enemy. Although much technical information has been published since the war the Atomic Energy Commission clings to much the same policy as did its predecessor. Naturally, V-J day removed many of the wraps about the atomic project and the Smyth Report revealed a wealth of detail about the work. However, any data bearing on the production plants at Oak Ridge or Hanford, or those at Paducah and at the Savannah River site, were kept closely guarded. All operations at the Los Alamos laboratory were similarly veiled in secrecy.

These operations might well have been kept from the public without any jeopardy to the nation's progress in atomic weapons if top-notch men had remained at their posts following the war. But when a new team, some of which may be second raters, infest and control a scientific establishment and operate behind a wall of secrecy those outside cannot criticize what goes on inside. Under these conditions the taxpayers' dollars may be wasted on second-rate work and no one is the wiser. This is especially true in military projects for the real state of affairs is never revealed until there is an emergency and by that time all is forgotten in the haste to rearm.

Security breaks usually occur at top level. Generals or admirals reveal the secret data at a Congressional hearing and simultaneously handouts are given to members of the press. People working on some secret projects are then astonished to find their work described on page one of the morning newspaper. A case in point was the Army's disclosure of atomic artillery.

The admirals and generals are not the only ones who deliberately violate security; congressmen are equally culpable. One has only to recall the monumental security break on the H-bomb. Some legislators are often anxious to break into the news with sensational stories to remind their constituents that they are big wheels in Washington. Others may divulge secret information given to them in an appropriations hearing without realizing they are violating security. Still others act in concert with military men to win public sympathy for a pet project. Together the leaks from the Pentagon and from Capitol Hill constitute the majority of the security violations. They make a mockery of secrecy for at high level the big secrets are revealed while at a low level little secrets are kept. There is no sense in such an ambivalent policy for it saddles our projects with the stultifying encumbrance of secrecy while telling the enemy what he wants to know most.

These military-Congressional disclosures of secret data are also dangerous for another reason. Too often the things revealed are weapons which are in the cocoon stage. It may take from three to five years for the weapon to hatch and emerge as a full-fledged instrument of war. A severe injustice is done to the American public when they are presented with stories about military weapons and led to believe that these gadgets are ready for use when in reality they are only in the incubation stage. The military cannot defend the United States with weapons they do not have. For example, in the field of guided missiles there have been many instances where the public has been misled into a false sense of security. Stories appearing in print assured the reader that American cities would be protected against enemy A-bombs through the magic of guided missiles which would unerringly seek out the invading bomber and "kill" it before it reached its target. Such stories have been rife ever since the war but the guided missiles are nowhere in evidence. Nor is this to be attributed to airtight secrecy. Incidentally, the real story behind our laggardly development of guided missiles would reveal the insidious effects of secrecy, showing the chaotic state of affairs resulting from the impact of the iron fist of the military on scientific development.

Atomic secrecy has had a paralyzing effect in the development of atomic power. Initially, the excuse which was given for lowering a blanket of secrecy over this new field was that atomic power plants can produce bomb material. Therefore, any improvement in a power plant would give the Russians a superior way to manufacture the material essential for atomic bombs. Furthermore, revealing details of the big plutonium production plants on the banks of the Columbia River would tell the Soviets how fast we were manufacturing plutonium and thus give them information about our atomic stockpile. The latter is the "holy of holies" among the bombs secrets. In fact, it is so secret that it was not to be entrusted to even the members of the Joint Congressional Atomic Energy Committee, the very people who do more to determine atomic policy than anyone else in the United States. It is a rather curious business, to say the least, when what amounts to the board of directors is not supposed to know how much product the business has produced. That the atomic stockpile is not the secret we think it is has been indicated by the late Senator McMahon, chairman of the elite committee, when he stated in the Bulletin of the Atomic Scientists that the stockpile could be estimated to within 15 per cent by a foreign power. If we accept this as fact then it would seem we conceal little from the enemy when we try to hide the details of our atomic production plants. But so stubbornly do our legislators cling to the concept of secrecy, although paradoxically they violate it regularly, there is little doubt that even if we had positive proof that the Soviets knew the size of our stockpile they would never look this fact in the face. Be this as it may, there is today another excuse given for enshrouding atomic power work in secrecy. The reason is that atomic power plants are of great potential value as propulsion devices for submarines, ships, and aircraft.

If by keeping atomic power under wraps we could be assured of making superior military devices then one might not object too strenuously to this secrecy. But when this lid of secrecy is clamped down on a project so tightly that it stifles the atmosphere inside and impedes progress then secrecy cannot be rationalized. Yet the secrecy which has attended atomic power development since V-J day has impeded our progress. This lack of forward motion in developing A-power plants was treated in the two chapters on A-power. Secrecy has very definitely inhibited industry from wholehearted participation in atomic development. As we have seen this work is largely engineering and industrial in flavor and industry could make a much greater contribution than it has in the past. There is no valid reason why industry could not be invited into A-power development on a completely nonsecret basis. By doing this we would add the stimulus of new ideas and we would provide a competitive spirit to atomic work. Competition and individual initative are the priceless ingredients which are today lacking in the monopoly of the Atomic Energy Commission.

Whatever advantages you may lose in abandoning a policy of airtight secrecy—and they seem very few—you more than compensate for them in the great impetus which nonsecret work gets from the outside world. You in effect stay ahead in an arms race not by plodding along with a static policy of secrecy but by driving ahead dynamically. You can even afford to advertise what you are doing for you depend not on secrets for security but upon achievement. American industry does not get fooled by secrecy. It does not stay in business by clutching secrets to its breast. Rather it wins out over competitors by putting out a superior product. In other words it operates on a policy of success through achievement. This is the American way of doing business.

There are certain things which properly should be kept secret and these generally pertain to operational matters such as troop movements, battle plans, intelligence, and over-all strategy. The trouble is that the military use a blanket type of secrecy which encompasses far more than military operations; it is extended to include equipment. Since no one draws the line secrecy is allowed to spread until it has a stranglehold on every single activity of a huge research center. Even basic research is kept classified. Dr. R. G. Gustavson, chancellor of Nebraska University, has warned against the folly of trying to keep the fundamentals of science secret pointing out that "When we start talking about secrets, which we do not possess—because as far as basic information is concerned, they are open—then we start to indicate that we do have a military advantage in terms of fundamental basic knowledge which we do not have, and we are lulling ourselves into a false sense of security." Probably uppermost in the educator's mind was the fact that most of the scientific principles upon which the A-bomb was based evolved in Europe and represented the work of many men of different nationalities.

We are prone to accept secrecy blindly without examining its nature or its effects. So far as the effects are concerned we have seen that they are detrimental to national security in many areas and of dubious value in others. Inquiring into the nature of a secret calls for some study of the anatomy of a secret. This we have already done somewhat indirectly but now we may briefly approach the issue frontally, asking what is the most important feature of a secret. The one which stands out is the time factor, that is really the object of secrecy—to gain time over an enemy. Those who dictate that a project should be secret do so in order that our nation will be able to keep the enemy from stealing our secrets and getting the weapon under development before we do. It is hoped that airtight security measures will keep the weapon from enemy eyes for many years. Implicit in this policy is the tacit assumption that the enemy cannot use his own talent and resources to produce the same development. Implicit also is a kind of egotism and arrogance which overestimates one's own ability while underestimating that of an enemy. We have already seen that the roots of science cannot be confined to any one land. What we can do others can do also. In fact, since secrecy breeds conservatism and discourages risks there is the very real possibility that while we are mesmerized by barbed wire and triple-locked safes the enemy may outdistance our own progress.

What, then, should we do about secrecy? Should we abandon all pretense at keeping secrets? No thinking person would urge that we swing to this extreme, for we do not want to make things easy for the Soviets. On the other hand, with too much secrecy we roadblock our own progress. Somewhere between "too much" and "too little" we must find a balance point. There is no question that we are now far out on the heavy or "too much" side of the scales.

We must take a good hard look at secrecy and determine precisely what things should really be kept secret. Then we should proceed to keep them secret as a hard core of data. Rigid penalties should be meted out to anyone violating security—be he scientist, senator, or general. The task of keeping the secrets will be easier because there will be fewer to guard. In weeding out those things which are not secret from those which are, three criteria should be used, remembering always that the objective is to keep from the Soviets that which would be of most value to them.

First, we should ask ourselves: "Can the secret really be kept?" It is folly to stamp papers secret if, by the very nature of the work, it is reasonable to assume that the Soviets either already have or will soon find out for themselves what is held secret. In this respect, we must recognize that there are some things, the electric light is an example, which to be useful cannot be kept secret.

Second, we must adopt the principle of the calculated risk in assessing what should be classified, balancing the positive value of keeping the data from the Russians against the negative value of withholding it from our own people. But, as in battle, we need men of courage to act boldly. Too often government bureaus are infested with men who cringe before the frowns of those on Capitol Hill.

Third, we must recognize that secrets cannot be kept indefinitely. A secret in science is not like a bar of gold which can be stored away at Fort Knox. More aptly, it is like a vegetable; it is perishable. The enemy can independently uncover the same data—and without espionage. This means that all classified files must be examined periodically to cull out those secrets which have "perished."

The current emergency has enmeshed much of the nation in a tight web of secrecy and supersecrecy. This condition which represents a stranglehold on science is not likely to change very soon. Yet it is imperative that secrecy be kept within bounds lest its effect be more to undermine the nation's security than to insure it.

12

POWER FOR THE FUTURE

As I write this final chapter, ten years have passed since the date of the world's first chain reaction in Chicago. During these years atomic energy has emerged as a lusty, if somewhat precocious, infant and by now it should be possible to foresee its future development.

Naturally, any assessment of this new force must take into account the prevailing world climate. Continuation of the deadlock between the East and the West with more and more emphasis on atomic armament will prejudice the peacetime development of atomic energy. In this final chapter we shall assume that world conditions will make it possible to focus more attention upon the nonmilitary atom. So, with the stipuation that war is not taken into account, let us look at atomic energy as it may be a boon to mankind in the future. Just what does the atom promise for the future?

Let me confess that I have no special crystal ball with which to divine the future. In fact, I have on my desk an opaque and quite ancient Chinese marble sphere to constantly remind me how murky the future is and how little the human eye can discern it. But we do have some substantial basis for making educated guesses about the long-range future of atomic energy. We have back of us ten full years of work on atomic energy and, while well over 90 per cent of our work has been of a military nature, still an enormous amount of work applicable to peacetime uses has been accomplished.

As far as it is possible to see, the real peacetime promise of atomic energy lies in the power which can be released from the atom. To be sure there will be by-products such as the radioisotopes which will find increasing and more important usefulness but the real pay-off of atomic energy will be power. This is because the atom gives the promise of power and because man is such a power-hungry creature. In 1952 the Materials Policy Commission submitted a voluminous report to the President and in it were detailed analyses of the energy resources and requirements of both this country and the rest of the world. For example, it contained the estimate that the next twenty-five years would see the demand for all fuels reach almost twice the 1950 levels. In the area of electrical power production the utilities industry estimates that by 1960 the nation's power capacity will be roughly three times what it was at the end of the last war. Commenting upon the rate of use-up of our natural fuels the President's Commission stated:

The time will come (in the not-too-distant future) when civilization's energy needs will outrun nature's declining store of fossil fuels available for economic use. Before this happens, ways must be found to harness economically such unconventional sources as solar and atomic energy.

Man must project his thoughts to the future and to the future increased demand for power. In a sense it is easier to look forward over a century or two than it is to try to assess the next several decades. If the heritage that we bequeath to future generations is one of depleted fuel reserves, of dry oil wells and exhausted basic mineral deposits then the citizens of the next century or the ones after that will curse our profligacy with nature. It is entirely possible and, indeed, probable that the greater populations of the earth only a few centuries from now will look back upon the twentieth century as the Age of Plenty when people had power to burn and raw materials to waste. With both power and materials in good supply we think of science and technology as forever on the upswing but the time can come when the rising curve will peak and start downhill. Then man's productivity will fall off and with this the world's food supply will go into the decline even as its population makes greater and greater demands upon the earth's fertility.

An obvious place for man to look for more power is the atom. He should not be unduly chagrined by the pessimism of the moment regarding the economic aspects of atomic energy or the fact that there may be no large-scale peacetime utilization of this energy within the next decade. We know that there is vastly more energy in a lump of uranium than there is in a lump of coal—roughly 2 million times more. And we know that we have it within our power to unlock this energy and set it to work. We are much less certain about the amounts of uranium which exist in nature and which can be economically exploited. There may not be another huge deposit like the rich Mother Lode in the Belgian Congo but there certainly are extensive deposits of lower-grade uranium ores. Until ten years or so ago there was not much incentive to hunt for uranium. Now that this lustrous pitchblende and the highly colored minerals of uranium are so much in demand the earth's surface will be scoured to turn up even deposits yielding only a few ounces of uranium per ton of ore. New chemical techniques will make it possible to work ores which up to now have been deemed worthless and this achievement will enormously increase the reserves of uranium available in the earth.

At the present time the best estimates show that the uranium reserves are much less in their energy content than our known coal reserves. Even taking into account the possibility of utilizing low-grade ores and the probability that breeding will be successful so that both the U-238 and U-235 fractions of uranium can be used it still appears that coal is our most bountiful supply of power. However, we must remember that our premium fuels, oil and natural gas, are being rapidly depleted. Uranium can and will substitute for these fuels in many industrial applications. It does not appear that you can count upon a uranium furnace in the basement to replace the gas or oil heating unit but, nonetheless, central station atomic power should be available well before the turn of the century.

Analyzing the impact of atomic power upon our national economy is obviously a job for skilled economists. The few who have seriously studied the over-all problem and who have not been dismayed by their brief encounters with the high potentates of atomic energy in the government do not seem to have taken a very optimistic view of atomic power. They maintain that this new power will not revolutionize the world, either socially or economically. They agree that the first use of A-power will occur in special industries like those involved in the production of glass, copper and aluminum. My own feeling is that most economists are too conservative or take too short a focus on the problem.

If we look beyond the rim of this century we should see a decided impact of atomic power upon the civilization of some countries, perhaps Russia more than others because that country has a real need for power. But it is also quite possible that atomic power may be developed early enough to help strengthen America's civilian economy when, and if, the present arms race slackens off or ends.

I believe that atomic power may be a decisive factor in locating the cities of the future. For example, since uranium power could bring abundant power to the minehead it should be possible to establish small cities near remote mineral deposits which require large amounts of power for their processing. The advent of economic A-power should go a long way toward freeing man from much of his previous dependence upon such natural facilities as proximity to waterways to assure cheap transportation of fuels and raw materials.

Furthermore, we should not overlook the possibility that atomic furnaces may provide the chemists and engineers with a new tool for entirely new chemical processing techniques. The higher temperatures available with atomic power may make it possible to open up a brand new field of chemical engineering.

The entire program of atomic power development in this country is based upon uranium furnishing heat which is then extracted from a nuclear reactor through conventional engineering techniques. In fact it is due partly to limitations of the latter that atomic power is so slow in reaching the American scene. Now no qualified physicist believes that electricity can be won directly from the uranium atom, that is, not on any economically practical basis. But some physicists hold out hope that the heat produced in a nuclear reactor can be used in an unconventional manner without being encumbered by all the limitations of heat exchangers, turbines, condensers, and all the equipment of conventional thermal engineering. The hope is that a means may be found to utilize the heat from the atom without making this detour. Scientists have some ideas about how this can be done but as yet they have not proved practicable. This does not mean, however, that something new may not turn up. In fact, in a new field such as atomic energy the unexpected should be expected. There is always the possibility of a new discovery, even of a development as revolutionary as fission, itself.

In looking to the future it is well to recognize that most scientists are extremely conservative in making any forecasts. Where they have few signposts to guide them they tend to be even more cagey about predictions. I recall that even the great Lord Rutherford, the father of experimental nuclear science, expressed the belief as late as 1937 that his studies in atomic energy would not be of practical value. Five years later the first chain reaction was achieved.

So far man has succeeded in merely scratching the surface of the energy which is locked up inside the atom. In uranium fission, for example, only one-tenth of one per cent of the atom's energy is tapped. In hydrogen fusion, only one-half of one per cent of the energy is given up. In other words over 99 per cent of the atom's energy is left untapped. This is because man today is only able to get at the energy which is released by a rearrangement of the particles inside the tiny nucleus of the atom. When a uranium nucleus fissions into two smaller fragments the total number of particles inside the nucleus of the parent and the daughter atoms does not change. The same is true of hydrogen fusion. Man taps only the difference in what we call the binding energies of the parent and daughter. If the particles themselves could be converted into energy then man would have as limitless a source of energy as the sun, itself.

Can man tap this *real* atomic energy? Can he get at the lion's share of the energy locked up in matter or must he always content himself with less than one per cent of this energy?

I have yet to meet a physicist who knows of any way in which this real nuclear energy can be harnessed. Maybe it will be impossible, as is the case with so many things which are important. But man has only just begun his concerted attack upon the nucleus. It is a strong citadel which yields its innermost secrets with the greatest of reluctance but someday it may yield its greatest of all secrets—the key to subnuclear energy. Then man will be truly master over nature. Personally, I think it highly unlikely that I shall live to see this day but one life span, or what is left of it, is a small time as civilization reckons it.

Whenever I think of the wonders of science and its promise for mankind I think of a remarkable statement by Winston Churchill, whose gift of prophecy is not without honor:

Man in this moment of his history has emerged in greater supremacy over the forces of nature than has ever been dreamed of before. He has it in his power to solve quite easily the problems of material existence. He has conquered the wild beasts, and he has even conquered the insects and the microbes. There lies before him, if he wishes, a golden age of peace and progress. All is in his hand. He has only to conquer his last and worst enemy—himself. With vision, faith and courage, it may still be within our power to win a crowning victory for all.

Index

Set in Linotype Times Roman
Format by Marguerite Swanton
Manufactured by The Haddon Craftsmen, Inc.
Published by HARPER & BROTHERS, *New York*